STANLEY
KUNITZ

SELECTED
POEMS

Winner of the Pulitzer Prize for poetry.

"His book shudders with life, and flings seeds in all directions . . . The publication of his SELECTED POEMS is, I believe, an event of major importance for everyone who cares about art and human civilization in this country. The book stands on the terrible threshold of greatness."

— James Wright
Sewanee Review

"The ageless themes of love, the changing seasons, and the inexorable tyranny of time are only part of the immense panorama of ___ he finest of living American poets."

ek

ATLANTIC-LITTLE, BROWN
ARE PUBLISHED BY
LITTLE, BROWN AND COMI
IN ASSOCIATION WITH
THE ATLANTIC MONTHLY P

Little, Brown and Company / Boston •

P9-DFF-568

ALSO BY JOHN BERGER

A
Fortunate
Man

The Story of a Country Doctor

John Berger
Jean Mohr

Introduction by Gavin Francis

CANONGATE

Edinburgh · London

This edition published in Great Britain in 2016 by Canongate Books Ltd,
14 High Street, Edinburgh EH1 1TE

First published in Great Britain in 1967 by Allen Lane,
The Penguin Press, Vigo Street, London W1

www.canongate.tv

2

British Library Cataloguing-in-Publication Data
A catalogue record for this book is available on
request from the British Library

ISBN 978 1 78211 503 8

Typeset in Goudy by Palimpsest Book Production Ltd,
Falkirk, Stirlingshire

Printed and bound in Great Britain by Clays Ltd, St Ives plc.

This book is dedicated to
John and Betty whom it concerns, and
to Philip O'Connor
for the letters he wrote to me whilst I was writing it.
J.B.

Introduction

A *Fortunate Man* is a masterpiece of witness; a three-way medita-
tion on humanity, society and the value of healing. First published
in 1967 it remains strikingly original, blending John Berger's text
with Jean Mohr's photographs in a series of superb reflections on
the doctor's role, the roots of cultural and intellectual deprivation,
and the motivations that drive medical practice. The subject of
the book, John 'Sassall', emerges as an individual deeply committed
to inner reflection as well as to his vocation as a physician. When
I was working as a newly qualified doctor it became my habit to
give copies as gifts. For years it's been out of print and increasingly
scarce; the habit was becoming expensive.

When asked how to approach his own work, Berger has often
replied, 'I'm a story-teller.' 'Even when I was writing on art,' he
said in 1984, 'it was really a way of story-telling – story-tellers
lose their identity and are open to the lives of other people.'*
When I went to meet Berger, to ask him how he and Mohr came
to create *A Fortunate Man*, he began by telling me a story.

It started in London, in the early 1950s, when Berger was a
commentator on art for the *New Statesman*. His essays and reviews
were unconventional as well as controversial; he had to fight to
keep his job. 'We received a marvellous essay from an Indian
writer called Victor Anant,' he told me, 'called "An English
Christmas". On the back of the envelope was the return address:
"Left Luggage Office, Paddington Station". I jumped on my motor-
bike and drove over to meet him. He'd not long arrived from
Bombay, and this was the first job he'd found.'

---

* Interview in *Marxism Today*, December 1984, with Geoff Dyer.

Anant, like Berger, distrusted established power; in India he had been imprisoned by the Raj. The two men became friends and, several years later when Berger was living in rural Gloucestershire, Anant and his Pakistani wife were drawn to live nearby. Sassall was the single-handed general practitioner who attended the two men at that time.

'I became friends with Sassall after going to him with some minor medical problem,' Berger explained. 'He cured me, and we became friends. I used to meet regularly with him and with Anant to play bridge.' The two writers recognised in Sassall an outstanding physician as well as the enthusiast of an unfashionable ideal – the Renaissance dream of aspiring to universal knowledge and experience. As a doctor who sought daily to empathise with others, though they be of very different backgrounds and perspectives, they perceived that Sassall came closer to attaining this ideal than most men or women ever could.

By the mid 1960s Berger had moved to Geneva, but both he and Anant were still in touch with Sassall. One day, Anant suggested that Berger write a book about their friend, his medical practice, and his determined pursuit of the universal. Berger again: '"You know, this man is really remarkable," Anant told me, "but one day no one will know of him. His goodness will have consequences, of course, but unless you write about him, the specifics of his life and his attitude may not be preserved."'

Jean Mohr was at that time also living in Geneva; a photojournalist with the Red Cross and the United Nations who had done some of his finest work documenting the stateless experience of Palestinian refugees. 'Jean is one of the *truly great* photographers,' Berger told me, 'utterly invisible, blending into the background like a lamp-stand – the perfect man to sit in on medical consultations.' Sassall invited Berger and Mohr to live with him and his family for six weeks and, with his patients' permission, join him night and day in the clinic and on emergency visits.

Afterwards the two men returned to Geneva and worked in isolation from one another for just a month – Berger recalls the text flowing fairly quickly. 'When we got together again, and compared what I'd written with the photographs Jean had chosen, we found we'd replicated one another's work entirely,' he said. 'They were tautologous – as if my text was a series of captions to his images. We had both tried to write the book on our own. That's not what we wanted at all, so we reworked it so that the words and pictures were like a conversation; building on, rather than mirroring, one another.' Sassall checked the manuscript and made some minor corrections – 'medical terminology, technical comments, that sort of thing' – but was otherwise happy with it. In April 1967 the book was published.

The *Guardian* carried an early review by Tom Maschler, the celebrated editor at Jonathan Cape, placed between a photograph of a Vietnamese baby scarred with napalm and an advertisement for woollen mini-dresses. 'It is a beautiful book', Maschler wrote, 'John Berger writes with a passion, with an intensity that few writers could achieve.' He is particularly entranced by the way Sassall, as portrayed by Berger, has an insatiable appetite for human experience, and imaginatively enters the minds of his patients. He closes with the lament that many reviewers feel when confronted by such a visionary and transformative work, but few have the courage to articulate: 'I only wish I could do justice in a few words to the richness that makes this book so compelling.'

Philip Toynbee, writing in the *Observer* a few days later, called it 'a series of brilliant descriptive sketches . . . a genuine *tour de force*, and the admirable photographs of the local countryside and its inhabitants match and illuminate the text with an unusual degree of sympathetic understanding'. Toynbee felt particularly well-qualified to comment on the accuracy of Berger's portrayal of the physician: the book's subject happened to be his own doctor.

'The Sassall who emerges from these pages – both from the text and from the photographs – is indeed the man that I myself have known, liked, and admired for several years. But he is more than the man I know, not because Berger has romanticised him or enlarged him, but because Berger knows him better than I do and has thought about him harder.'

A *Fortunate Man* is a memorial not just to this exceptional individual but to a way of practising medicine that has almost disappeared. Sassall's approach to his practice is all-consuming – in today's culture of working-time-directives and the commercialisation of disease it would be almost impossible to sustain. Sassall has made a Faustian pact: he is rewarded with endless opportunities for experiencing the possibilities inherent in human lives, but at the cost of being subject to immense, and at times unbearable pressures. These pressures manifest themselves as episodes of profound depression, periods during which he is overwhelmed by 'the suffering of his own patients and his own sense of inadequacy'.

The book opens with a series of 'case studies', though the term is too clinical and doesn't reflect either the emotional subtlety of Berger's word-sketches or the versatility of Sassall's responsiveness to his patients. They are glimpses of the situations Sassall responds to every day, recognisable to any doctor, but they convey the extraordinary depth of Sassall's commitment to his patients. They tell of the struggles of those patients, and also show how powerful an influence the landscape exerts on the community and its stories. As Berger writes in the opening pages: 'Sometimes a landscape seems to be less a setting for the life of its inhabitants than a curtain behind which their struggles, achievements and accidents take place.' Within that landscape the community looks to Sassall as a 'clerk of records'; the figure to whom they tell their stories: 'He keeps the records so that, from time to time, they can consult them themselves.'

Berger and Mohr follow Sassall through these parallel landscapes – the physical landscape of rural England and the metaphorical one of his patients' lives. The moral possibilities of medical practice are drawn out, without shying away from the risks that doctors like Sassall run in identifying so closely with those suffering mental and physical pain. The myth of Faust, the life of Paracelsus, the works of Conrad, and the dream of the universal are each examined for the ways they illuminate aspects of Sassall's motivation. He is compared to one of Conrad's Master Mariners who sets out to compass not the globe, but the totality of human experience.

Towards the end Berger tries to make an assessment of Sassall's contribution to society and his community, but finds that he cannot. A society that doesn't know how to value the lives of its people can't adequately account for the value of easing their pain. 'What is the social value of a pain eased?' Berger asks, 'What is the value of a life saved? How does the cure of a serious illness compare in value with one of the better poems of a minor poet? How does making a correct but extremely difficult diagnosis compare with painting a great canvas?' The absurdity of the questions reveals just how far we have to go in appreciating the value not just of art, but of life.

In the years after publication Berger moved to Haute Savoie, a remote Alpine district in the south-east of France close to the Swiss and Italian borders, in order to live closely with people who worked the land. 'I didn't go to university,' he told me, 'the peasants were my university professors.' Like Sassall in rural Gloucestershire, Berger became a 'clerk of records' for the people he came to live amongst. He poured his reflections on their lives into his trilogy *Into Their Labours*, as well as works such as *The Seventh Man*: his exposition, again with Mohr, of Europe's exploitation of peasant migrant labour. As a story-teller, Berger wishes to lose his identity in that of his subject and his readers, just as Sassall sought to lose his identity in those of his patients. His assessment of Sassall could stand for an assessment of his own life and work: 'Like an artist or like anybody else who believes that his work justifies his life, Sassall – by our society's miserable standards – is a fortunate man.'

A few years after *A Fortunate Man* was written Sassall's wife died unexpectedly. At the end of his *Observer* review, Philip Toynbee confessed to a 'quarrel' with Berger for leaving her out of the narrative, though the book is dedicated in part to her: 'this racked and pain-haunted man would have collapsed long ago, and perhaps irretrievably, if it hadn't been for his wife,' Toynbee wrote, 'Her role is as archetypal as his.' Following her death Sassall left the Gloucestershire practice and travelled for some time in China, learning the ways of the barefoot doctors who were then the main providers of medical care in rural China. His death in 1982, alluded to in Berger's own postscript, deepens the enigma of his life. A careful reading of *A Fortunate Man* reveals its title to be a paradox; fitting for a study of a man whose very openness to experience – his gift to the world – may also have been his undoing.

A Fortunate Man is almost fifty years old, but remains fresh, urgent and relevant; a reminder for physicians and patients alike of the essence of medical practice – of the differences between healing and medicating. It is a text with resonance for anyone who admires Sassall's pursuit of the universal. Like all great works it is many things: a celebration of a way of medicine that we have all but lost, a ground-breaking exercise in photo-documentary, a literary-photographic creation of lasting beauty and a personal study of a man who aspired to an impossible ideal. Sassall's goal was an intimate appreciation of what it means to be human; medicine was just the vehicle he chose to reach it. In my own work as a general practitioner his kindness and imaginative empathy are an inspiration, but at the same time he stands as a warning of what can happen when boundaries between a physician and his or her patients breaks down.

In trying to assess Sassall's qualities as a physician Berger wrote 'he is acknowledged as a good doctor because he meets the deep but unformulated expectation of the sick for a sense of fraternity'. This quest for recognition, and for a sense of fraternity, has rarely been articulated so beautifully. Back in 1967, Tom Maschler concluded his *Guardian* review of *A Fortunate Man* saying simply: 'I am grateful for it.' I too am grateful: to Victor Anant for suggesting the book in the first place, to John Berger and Jean Mohr for crafting such a masterpiece, and of course to Sassall, and his family, for permitting the intimate details of his life and attitudes to be set down. Through this new edition I hope many more readers come to know that gratitude.

Gavin Francis

A
Fortunate
Man

Landscapes can be deceptive. Sometimes a landscape seems to be less a setting for the life of its inhabitants than a curtain behind which their struggles, achievements and accidents take place.

For those who, with the inhabitants, are behind the curtain, landmarks are no longer only geographic but also biographical and personal.

One of them shouted a warning, but it was too late. The leaves brushed him down almost delicately. The small branches encaged him. And then the tree and the whole hill crushed him together.

A man breathlessly said that a woodman was trapped beneath a tree. The doctor asked the dispenser to find out exactly where: then suddenly picked up his own phone, interrupted her and spoke himself. He must know exactly where. Which was the nearest gate in the nearest field? Whose field? He would need a stretcher. His own stretcher had been left in hospital the day before. He told the dispenser to phone immediately for an ambulance and tell it to wait by the bridge which was the nearest point on the road. At home in the garage there was an old door off its hinges. Blood plasma from the dispensary, door from the garage. As he drove through the lanes he kept his thumb on the horn the whole time, partly to warn oncoming traffic, partly so that the man under the tree might hear it and know that the doctor was coming.

After five minutes he turned off the road and drove uphill, into the mist. As often up there above the river, it was a very white mist, a mist that seemed to deny all weight and solidity. He had to stop twice to open gates. The third gate was already slightly open, so he drove through it without stopping. It swung back and crashed against the rear of the Land Rover. Some sheep, startled, appeared and disappeared into the mist. All the while he had his thumb on the horn for the woodman to hear. After one more field he saw a figure waving behind the mist – as if he were trying to wipe clean a vast steamed-up window.

When the doctor reached him the man said: 'He's been screaming ever since. He's suffering something terrible doctor.' The man would tell the story many times, and the first would be tonight in the village. But it was not yet a story. The advent of the doctor brought the conclusion much nearer, but the accident was not yet over: the wounded man was still screaming at the other two men who were hammering in wedges preparatory to lifting the tree.

'Christ let me alone.' As he cried 'alone' the doctor was beside him. The wounded man recognized the doctor; his eyes focused. For him too the conclusion was nearer and this gave him the courage to be quieter. Suddenly it was silent. The men had stopped hammering but were still kneeling on the ground. They knelt and looked at the doctor. His hands are at home on a body. Even these new wounds which had not existed twenty minutes before were familiar to him. Within seconds of being beside the man he injected morphine. The three onlookers were relieved by the doctor's presence. But now his very sureness made it seem to them that he was part of the accident: almost its accomplice.

'He had a chance,' said one of the kneeling men, 'when Harry here shouted but he went and turned about the wrong way.'

The doctor set up the plasma for a transfusion into the arm. As he moved around, he explained what he was doing to try to reassure the others.

'I shouted at him,' said Harry, 'he could have got clear if he'd looked sharp.'

'He would have got clear like that,' said the third.

As the morphine worked, the wounded man's face relaxed and his eyes closed. It was then as though the relief he felt was so intense that it reached the others.

'He's lucky to be alive,' said Harry.

'He could have got clear like that,' said the third.

The doctor asked them if they could shift the tree.

'I reckon we can if we are three now.'

Nobody was kneeling any longer. The three woodsmen were standing, impatient to begin. The mist was getting whiter. The moisture was condensing on the half-empty bottle of plasma. The doctor noticed that this fractionally changed its colour, making it look yellower than normal.

'I want you to lift,' he said, 'while I put a splint on his leg.'

When the wounded man felt the reverberations in the tree as they levered it, he began to moan again.

'We could injure him worse than ever,' said Harry, 'getting him out.' He could see the crushed leg underneath like a dog killed on the road.

'Just hold it steady,' said the doctor.

Again the doctor, whom they knew so well, seemed the accomplice of disaster as he worked under the tree on the leg the fourth of them would lose.

'We'd never believed you'd got here so quick, doc,' said the third.

'You know Sleepy Joe?' asked the doctor. 'He was trapped under a tree for twelve hours before any help came.'

He gave instructions on how to lift the wounded man on to the door and then into the back of the Land Rover.

'You'll be all right now Jack,' said one of them to the wounded man whose face was as damp and pallid as the mist. The third touched his shoulder.

The ambulance was waiting at the bridge. When it had driven off, Harry turned to the doctor confidentially.

'He's lost his leg,' he said, 'hasn't he?'

'No, he won't lose his leg,' said the doctor.

The woodman walked slowly back up to the forest. As he climbed he put a hand on each thigh. He told the other two what the doctor had told him. As they worked there during the day stripping the tree, they noticed again and again the hollow in the ground where he had been trapped. The fallen leaves there were so dark and wet that it was impossible to distinguish the blood. But every time they noticed the place they questioned whether the doctor could be right.

She is a woman of about thirty-seven. There is just still about her the air of a schoolgirl: one of the less bright girls who is physically more developed than the others but whose physical maturity has already made her slow and maternal rather than shifting and sexy. There is just the last trace of this air about her. In two years it will have vanished. She looks after her mother and it is now for the mother rather than the daughter that the doctor usually visits the cottage.

He first saw the daughter ten years ago. She had a cold and cough and complained that she felt weak. Her chest X-ray was normal. He had the impression that she wanted to talk about something. She would never look at him directly but kept casting him quick anxious glances as though somehow by these to bring him closer. He questioned her but could not gain her confidence.

A few months later she was suffering from insomnia and then asthma. All the tests for allergy proved negative. The asthma got worse. Now when he saw her, she smiled at him through her illness. Her eyes were round like a rabbit's. She was timid of anything outside the cage of her illness. If anybody approached too near her eyes twitched like the skin round a rabbit's nose. But her face was quite unlined. He was convinced that her condition was the result of extreme emotional stress. Both she and her mother insisted, however, that she had no worries.

Two years later he discovered the explanation by chance. He was out on a maternity case in the middle of the night. There were three women neighbours in attendance. Whilst waiting he had a cup of tea with them in the kitchen. One of them worked in a large mechanized dairy in the nearest railway town. The girl with asthma had once worked there too. And it turned out that the manager – who was in the Salvation Army – had had an affair with her. Evidently he had promised to marry her. Then he was overcome by remorse and religious scruples and had abandoned her. Was it even an affair – or did he only once, one evening, lead her by the hand out of the creamery up to his leather-chaired office?

The doctor once again questioned the girl's mother. Had her daughter been happy when she worked at that dairy? Yes, perfectly. He asked the girl if she had been happy there. She smiled in her cage and nodded her head. Then he asked her outright if the manager had ever made a pass at her. She froze – like an animal who realizes that it is impossible to bolt. Her hands stopped moving. Her head remained averted. Her breathing became inaudible. She never answered him.

Her asthma continued and caused structural deterioration of the lungs. She now survives on steroids. Her face is moon-shaped. The expression of her large eyes is placid. But her brows and eyelids and the skin pulled tight over her cheekbones twitch at every movement and sound which might constitute a warning of the unexpected. She looks after her mother, but very seldom leaves the cottage. When she sees the doctor, she smiles at him as now she would probably smile at the soldier of the Salvation Army.

Before, the water was deep. Then the torrent of God and the

man. And afterwards the shallows, clear but constantly disturbed, endlessly irritated by their very shallowness as though by an allergy. There is a bend in the river which often reminds the doctor of his failure.

English autumn mornings are often like mornings nowhere else in the world. The air is cold. The floorboards are cold. It is perhaps

this coldness which sharpens the tang of the hot cup of tea.
Outside, steps on the gravel crunch a little more loudly than a

month ago because of the very slight frost. There is a smell of toast. And on the block of butter small grains of toast from the last impatient knife. Outside, there is sunlight which is simultaneously soft and very precise. Every leaf of each tree seems separate.

She lay in a four-poster bed: her face was ashen-coloured and her cheeks fallen in. Her eyes were tight shut in pain. She wheezed as she breathed, especially when breathing out.

The doctor stood looking and then asked for a cupful of warm water and cotton wool. As he injected morphia into her upper arm, she flinched a little. Strange that suffering so much pain in her chest she should flinch at the pin-prick. With the warm water and cotton wool he cleaned away the little droplet of blood from her worn, large arm, the colour of stone or bread, as though it had acquired the colour through its scrubbing and baking.

Then, using the same much-worked arm, he took her blood pressure. It was very low. She kept her eyes shut as if the light, so soft and so precise, was pressing between them. She had still said nothing.

He prepared a syringe for another injection. The fifty-year-old daughter was standing at the foot of the bed, waiting to be told what to do.

He inserted the needle into a vein near the wrist. This time she didn't flinch. After half the injection he paused, holding the syringe in the loose fold of skin as if it were the skin's feather, and with his other hand he felt her neck to check the strength of her pulse in the artery and the degree of congestion in the jugular vein. He then completed the injection.

The old woman opened her eyes. 'It's not your fault,' she said very distinctly, almost crisply.

He listened to her chest. Her overworked brown arms, her deeply lined face, her creased strained neck were suddenly denied by the soft whiteness of her breast. The grey-haired son down in the yard with the cows, the daughter at the foot of the bed in carpet slippers and with swollen ankles, had both once clambered and fed here, and yet the soft whiteness of her breast was like a young girl's. This she had preserved.

Downstairs in the parlour the doctor explained the medicines he was leaving. The old woman's wheezing was still audible through the floorboards. Three dogs lay on the carpet, heads on outstretched paws, eyes open. They scarcely stirred when the old man came in.

He seemed dazed and sleepy. The doctor asked him how he was. 'Not so bad,' he said, 'except for the screws.'

Neither father nor daughter nor the son outside asked the doctor about the old woman. The doctor said he would be coming back that evening.

When he came back the parlour was in darkness. This disturbed him somewhat. He called out and receiving no answer felt his way up the stairs. The stairs led straight into the first bedroom. Across it he could see the light under the door of the second room.

The room smelt now of sickness: under the dressing-table on which stood all the family wedding photographs in leather frames and a nineteenth-century child's mug with the Death and Burial of Cock Robin engraved upon it, there was an enamel bowl with urine in it, and spit stained a little with blood. The daughter explained that every time her mother coughed she peed a little involuntarily. The old woman was paler and a piece of damp rag was laid over her forehead. The room smouldered around her, all its comfort burnt and drenched and then burnt again.

The doctor listened once more to her chest. She lay back exhausted. 'I am sorry,' she said, not as though it were an apology but simply a fact. He took her temperature and blood pressure. 'I know,' he said, 'but you'll sleep soon and feel rested.'

Her husband was sitting in the dark in the next room. The doctor had walked through it without noticing him, when he had come up the stairs. Now the daughter shepherded both men down, but still without putting a light on. For a moment it seemed that the stairs and the parlour were part of the outbuildings, unlit, unheated, belonging to the animals now stabled for the night. It seemed that the home was reduced to the four-poster bed in the lighted room above, where the old woman, the soft whiteness of whose breast had never changed, was dying.

When the daughter suddenly switched the light on, the doctor and the old man were dazzled. For each of them it was like finding himself on a stage. The familiar furniture was part of a stage set and both had to play roles which were utterly strange to what they thought of as their true nature. Both would have grasped any chance of reverting to the normal truth.

The old man sat down with an overcoat across his knees. 'She has pneumonia now,' the doctor said, 'and she must take another medicine beside the ones I gave you this morning. Do you think she can swallow these pills? They are rather large. Or would she prefer to take it in liquid form? The liquid is made up for children but we can increase the dose. Which do you think would be best?'

The daughter, submissive and finding her only slight hope in trust, said: 'It's up to you doctor.'

'No it's not,' he said. 'I'm asking you. Can she or can she not swallow these pills?'

'Perhaps the liquid then,' said the daughter, abandoning her small hope. The doctor also gave her some sleeping pills – for her father as well as her mother. They would at least sleep tonight under the same drug.

The old man, whilst the doctor was explaining the medicines to the daughter, sat looking in front of him, his hands clutching and unclutching the heavy material of the overcoat across his knees.

When the doctor had finished his explanations, there was a silence. Neither father nor daughter moved to show him out or ask when he would be coming again. They simply waited. The doctor said, 'The immediate danger is past – another half hour and she might have died this morning, now she's got to pay the price of surviving the attack.'

'It sounds a funny mixture,' said the old man without looking up, 'heart trouble and then pneumonia. A funny mixture. She was quite well yesterday.' He began to cry, very quietly, like a woman can: the tears welling up in his eyes.

The doctor, who had already picked up one of his bags, put it down again and leant back in the chair. 'Can you make us a cup of tea?' he said

While the daughter was making the tea the two men spoke about the orchard at the back and this year's apples. When the daughter was there, they spoke about the father's rheumatism. After the tea the doctor went.

The next morning was another autumn morning like the preceding. Every leaf of each tree seemed separate. The sunshine, filtered through a tree in the orchard, played on the floor of the old woman's bedroom. She clambered out of bed and suffered a second attack. The doctor arrived within a quarter of an hour. Her lips were purple, her face clay-coloured. She died quickly, her hands very still.

In the parlour the old man rocked on his feet. The doctor deliberately did not put out a hand to steady him. Instead he faced him. The older man was the taller by nine inches. The doctor said quietly, his eyes extra wide behind his spectacles, 'It would have been worse for her if she'd lived. It would have been worse.'

He might have said that there have been kings and presidents of republics who have never recovered from the death of their wives. He might have said that death is the condition of life. He might have said that man is indivisible and that, in his own view, this was the only sense in which death could have no dominion.

But whatever he said at that moment, the old man would have continued to rock on his feet, until the daughter lowered him into his chair in front of the unlit fire.

Only her feet betray her. There is something about the way she walks on her feet – a kind of irresponsibility towards them – which is still quite childish. Her figure is 36–25–36.

She was crying when she came into the surgery.

'What's wrong Duckie?'

'I just feel sort of miserable.'

She sat like other girls had sat there crying because they thought they were pregnant. To make it easier for her, the doctor slipped the question between several others.

'What's getting you down?'

No answer.

'Sore throat?'

'Not now.'

'Water-works all right?'

She nodded.

'Have you got a temperature?'

She shook her head.

'Periods regular?'

'Yeah.'

'When was your last one?'

'Last week.'

The doctor paused.

'Do you remember that rash you used to get on your tum? Has it ever come back?'

'No.'

He leant forward in his chair towards her.

'You just feel weepy?'

She inclined her head farther towards her own consoling bosom.

'Did Mum and Dad put you up to come to me?'

'No, I came myself.'

'Even having your hair dyed didn't make you feel better?'

She laughed a little because he had noticed. 'It did for a while.'

The doctor took her temperature, looked at her throat and told her to stay in bed for two days. Then he resumed the conversation.

'Do you like working in that laundry?'

'It's a job.'

'What about the other girls there?'

'I don't know.'

'Do you get on with them?'

'You get stopped if they find you talking.'

'Have you thought of doing anything else?'

'What can I do?'

'What would you like to do?'

'I'd like to do secretarial work.'

'Who would you like to be secretary to?'

She laughed and shook her head.

Her face was grubby with tear stains. But around her eyes and in the muzzle of her face which terminates in her full lip-sticked lips there is evidence of the same force that has filled out her bust and her hips. She is nubile in everything except her education and her chances.

'When you're a bit better I'll keep you off work for a few days, if you like, and you can go to the Labour Exchange and find out how you can get trained. There are all kinds of training schemes.'

'Are there?' she said moonily.

'How did you do at school?'

'I wasn't any good.'

'Did you take O-levels?'

'No. I left.'

'But you weren't stupid were you?' He asked this as though if she admitted that she was, it would somehow reflect badly on him.

'No, not stupid.'

'Well,' he said.

'It's terrible that laundry. I hate it.'

'It's no good being sorry for yourself. If I give you a week off, will you really use it?'

She nodded, chewing her damp handkerchief.

'You can come up again on Wednesday and I'll phone the Labour Exchange and we'll talk about what they say.'

'I'm sorry,' she said, beginning to cry again.

'Don't be sorry. The fact that you're crying means you've got imagination. If you didn't have imagination, you wouldn't feel so bad. Now go to bed and stay there tomorrow.'

Through the surgery window he saw her walking up the lane to the common, to the house in which he had delivered her sixteen years ago. After she had turned the corner, he continued to stare at the stone walls on either side of the lane. Once they were dry walls. Now their stones were cemented together.

He had heard rumours about them. That they were on the run. That she was a prostitute from London. That the Council would have to act to turn them out of the abandoned cottage which the owner, a farmer, had given them permission to use (some said because he had met the girl in London) but in which they were living like squatters.

Three children were playing by the back door with some chicken wire. The mother was in the kitchen. She was a woman in her late twenties with long black hair, thin long hands and grey eyes that were both bright and very liquid. Her skin had an unwashed look which is more to do with anaemia than dirt.

'You won't be able to stay here in the winter,' he said.

'Jack says he's going to patch it up when he gets the time.'

'It needs more than patching up.'

There was a table in the kitchen and two chairs. By the stone sink there was an orange-box cupboard with some cups and plates and packets in it. Half the window above the sink was broken and there was a piece of cardboard across it. The sunshine streamed through the other half and the grey dust slowly rose and fell through the beam, so slowly that it seemed to be part of another uninhabited world.

Later in the front room she sat down on the bed and allowed herself to ask the question for which she had really sent for him.

'Doctor, can a woman of my age have heart trouble?'

'It's possible. Did you ever have rheumatic fever when you were a child?'

'I don't think so. But I get so out of breath. And if I bend down to pick something up, I can scarcely stand up proper again.'

'Let me have a listen. Just pull up your blouse.'

She wore a very worn black lace petticoat. The room was as little furnished as the kitchen. There was a large bed in one corner with some blankets on it and some more blankets on the floor. There was also a chest of drawers with a clock on it and a transistor radio. The windows were overgrown with thick ivy and since there was no plaster ceiling and holes in the rafters, the room scarcely seemed geometric and was more like a hide in a wood.

'We'll examine you properly when you come up to the surgery but I can promise you now that you haven't got a serious heart disease.'

'Oh I'm so relieved.'

'You can't go on like this. You know that don't you? We've got to get you out of here –'

'There's lots more unfortunate than us,' she said.

The doctor laughed, and then so did she. She was still young enough for her face to change totally with her expression. Her face looked capable of surprise again.

'If I won the football pools,' she said, 'I'd buy a big house and start a big home for children, but they say they make all kinds of difficulties these days for that kind of thing.'

'Where were you living before you came here?'

'In Cornwall. It was lovely there by the sea. Look.'

She opened the top drawer of the chest and from among her own stockings and children's socks she took out a photograph. It showed herself in high-heeled shoes, a tight skirt and a chiffon scarf round her head with a man and a small child walking along a beach.

'That's your husband?'

'No, that's not Jack, that's Cliff and Stephen.'

The doctor nodded, surprised.

'I'll say that for Jack,' she continued, 'he never makes no distinction between the kids that are his and those that are mine like. We share fifty-fifty. He's better to Steve than his own father. It's just that he can't touch me.'

She looked at the photograph, holding it out at arm's length.

The doctor asked whether she and her husband wanted to stay in the area and what would they think if he tried to get them a Council house. She answered without glancing away from the photo.

'You have to ask Jack about that. We do everything fifty-fifty.'

Still holding the photograph she let her arm fall on to her lap and looked at the doctor, her eyes now angry.

'Can you tell me if I'm too old? Jack says I'm too old. I only want it every two or three months.'

'That's all to do with your being tired and feeling you can't cope.'

'I've had a bellyful all right. Sometimes I think I just can't go on. I just want to lie down and stop.'

She got up and put the photograph back in the drawer. 'Do you like music?' she said and switched the radio on. Then after a few bars, she switched it off. She stood there against the chest, a quite different expression on her face: as though switching the radio on and off had reminded her of something.

'It just doesn't mean anything to me. It doesn't touch me. When he makes love to me it's like a wet rag across my face. I know what real love is like you see. With the father of Stephen, when I got Stephen it was beautiful. We came together and I was able to come to him with all of me. I know what they mean when they say it is the most wonderful thing in the world, it was like that when I got Stephen because I could come to him and he wanted me like that. And I shall never forget it – I lie awake and think of it yet – because it has never been like that again when it was like heaven when I got Stephen.'

We fell in love with it ten years ago – for the view. And I must say we've never regretted it, not even in the winter. It's so peaceful. Do you know last spring when I was walking along the path from the village I saw something standing in the front gate. I could see it as I turned the corner by the wood. It looked like a dog but it didn't, if you know what I mean. And do you know what it was? It was a badger. It just stood there between the gate-posts and stared at me. I didn't know what to do. Can they be dangerous? I just didn't know. Hugh was playing golf and so I went to ask Mr Hornby, and he came back with me, but by that time it had gone. But that isn't the end of the story. The badger has come to stay I think. He's invited himself. You remember the deep snow we had last winter, I don't know what we'd have done then without Mr Hornby, he cleared the path through the wood, otherwise you just couldn't get through, it was up to my waist, and it was very cold too, the cold was cruel, anyway as I was saying in the night I used to hear something on the roof, something moving about, I woke up Hugh several times and he said it was the snow shifting but I knew it wasn't because it was too cold you see for the snow to be moving, and in the morning I went to look and do you know there were his footsteps in the snow on the roof, would you believe it?

I suppose he was so cold up there in the wood behind that he came down in the dark for a bit of warmth. He could have nestled up against the chimney – Hugh says not, but I'm sure he could – and got nice and warm. I often think of him up there when I'm sitting by the fire thinking. Of course it's silly but you can see what I mean about it being very peaceful, can't you? I mean you wouldn't get badgers in Birmingham where we used to live when Hugh was still at work . . .' she continues endlessly.

When she phones it is usually about him rather than herself.

'I'm worried about him, doctor, he's got a pain in his back and I think it might be a slipped disk. It all came on in that wet spell last week when he insisted upon digging the vegetable garden, the first chance for two months, he said, and now he can't straighten up.'

Sometimes it sounds more serious.

'He's been in bed for three days and he has great difficulty in breathing. When he breathes at night – and I simply can't get to sleep listening to him – I keep on thinking he's talking, his breathing sounds like words, doctor.'

She is there at the door waiting.

'I'm so glad you've come. His whole body is collapsing. I better let you talk to him yourself, because he won't tell me what he's complaining of, he won't come out with it, he's funny like that you know, he just says all his organs are going. Which? I say. What do you mean? But he won't tell me, he just says all his organs.'

The husband, aged seventy-three, explains that he can't hold his water and that he has some pain in the lower part of the abdomen. The doctor checks his chest and stomach. He does a rectal examination to feel the prostate and to discover whether any growth is pressing on the bladder. He tests the urine for sugar and albumen. The sugar is just problematic. He diagnoses a mild urinary infection.

Thirty-six hours later she phones.

'He just can't take any liquid at all now. He can't drink. He hasn't taken a drop since yesterday breakfast. And he keeps on falling asleep. Right in the middle of my talking to him he just falls off – I don't know what to do. He just can't keep awake, not even when I'm talking to him, he just falls asleep and then he's sleepy and he falls asleep again even when I'm talking to him.'

The doctor smiles into the phone. Yet, just conceivably, if almost impossibly, the sleeping might be the beginning of a diabetic coma: the diabetes made manifest by the urinary infection. To be certain he must do another blood test for sugar.

At that gate where the badger stood, he pauses and looks down at the view with which they fell in love, and then he remembers her saying in a more intense, more sibilant voice than her ordinary one:

'All we've got is each other. So we have to be very strict. We watch over each other carefully when we are ill, we do.'

It is apart from the house: a building the size of two garages. It consists of a waiting-room, two consulting rooms and a dispensary. It is on the side of the hill which overlooks the river and the large wooded valley. From the other side of the valley it is almost too small to be visible.

On the door of the building is a notice which reads: Dr John Sassall M.B., Ch.B., D.Obst.R.C.O.G.

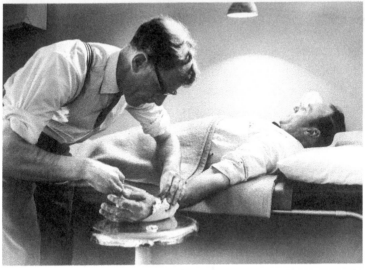

The consulting rooms do not seem clinical. They seem lived-in and cosy. But they are neater than most living-rooms and, despite their smallness, there is more clear space. This is the working area where the patient is examined or treated or manipulated.

The rooms remind one of a ship's officer's cabin. There is the same cosiness, the same ingenuity in fitting many things into a small space, the same odd juxtaposition of domestic furniture and personal effects with instruments and appliances.

All this makes the examining couch look like a bunk. It has two sheets on it and an electric blanket. Whenever patients are due, Sassall switches the blanket on a quarter of an hour beforehand, so that if a patient has to strip and be examined, it will not strike as cold. He has a fastidious sense for detail. He is a short man; the chair in which the patients sit is exactly six inches lower than his own chair by the desk. Before he gives an injection he says: 'You'll just feel a tap.' As his hand comes down, holding the syringe, he opens his little finger and with the side of his hand flicks hard against the skin by the side of where the needle will go in a fraction of a second later, and this distracts the patient from registering the prick of the needle.

The surgery is unusually well equipped. There is stoving equipment for sterilizing and the instruments necessary for the suture of tendons, minor amputations, the removal of cysts, cauterization of the cervix, the application and removal of plaster for minor fractures. There is an anaesthetic machine: an osteopathic table: a sigmoidoscope. He says that he is constantly frustrated because he has not got his own X-ray plant or his own equipment for elementary bacteriology.

If possible, he always wants to prove everything for himself.

Once he was putting a syringe deep into a man's chest: there was little question of pain but it made the man feel bad: the man tried to explain his revulsion: 'That's where I live, where you're putting that needle in.' 'I know,' Sassall said, 'I know what it feels like. I can't bear anything done near my eyes, I can't bear to be touched there. I think that's where I live, just under and behind my eyes.'

As a boy Sassall was much influenced by the books of Conrad. Against the boredom and complacency of middle-class life ashore in England, Conrad offered the 'unimaginable' whose instrument was the sea. Yet in this offered poetry there was nothing unmanly or effete: on the contrary, the only men who could face the unimaginable were tough, controlled, taciturn and outwardly ordinary. The quality which Conrad constantly warns against is at the same time the very quality to which he appeals: the quality of imagination. It is almost as though the sea is the symbol of this contradiction. It is to the imagination that the sea appeals: but to face the sea in its unimaginable fury, to meet its own challenge, imagination must be abandoned, for it leads to self-isolation and fear.

What resolves the contradiction and, in resolving it, places the whole drama on a level incomparably higher and more noble than the average petty life of self-seeking advancement, is the ideal of service. This ideal has a double meaning. The Service stands for all those traditional values which a privileged few who have faced and met the challenge esteem: esteem not as an abstract principle but as the very condition of practising their craft efficiently. And at the same time service also stands for the responsibility which the few must always carry for the many who depend upon them – the passengers, the crew, the traders, the ship-owners, the brokers.

Of course I simplify. And Conrad would not be the great artist he is if this were a fair summary of his attitude to the sea. But the simplification is enough to allow us to see why Conrad might appeal to a boy who was in revolt against his middle-class family background but who had no interest in becoming a Bohemian. He admired physical prowess. He enjoyed being practical and using his hands. He was inquisitive about things rather than feelings. He was stirred – like many boys of his class and generation – by the ideal of a moral example which might shame the opportunism of his elders.

In fact by the age of fifteen he had decided to become a doctor rather than a sailor. His father was a dentist and consequently he had the opportunity of meeting doctors socially. When he was fourteen he was already hanging round the dispensary of the local doctor: nominally helping to wrap up medicine bottles, actually trying to listen to the consultations taking place in the next room. Yet a doctor can well be imagined as the equivalent of a Master Mariner.

Sassall's image of a doctor at that time was:

'A man who was all-knowing but looking haggard. Once a doctor came in the middle of the night and I could see that he slept too – his pyjama trousers were poking out through the bottom of his trousers. But above all I remember he was in command and composed – whereas everybody else was fussing and agitated.'

Compare this to Conrad's first introduction of the captain of the *Narcissus*:

Captain Allistoun, serious, and with an old red muffler round his throat, all day long pervaded the poop. At night, many times he rose out of the darkness of the companion, such as a phantom above a grave, and stood watchful and mute under the stars, his night-shirt fluttering like a flag – then, without a sound, sank down again. . . . . He, the ruler of that minute world, seldom descended from the Olympian heights of his poop. Below him – at his feet, so to speak – common mortals led their busy and insignificant lives.

In both impressions there is the same sense of authority: an authority which pyjama trousers or a night-shirt in no way diminish. Or consider Conrad's description of one of the worst moments in *Typhoon*. With the exception of the one word *gale*, it might describe the crisis of an illness, with the voice of Captain MacWhirr transformed into that of a doctor.

And again he heard that voice, forced and ringing feebly, but with a penetrating effect of quietness in the enormous discord of noises, as if sent out from some remote spot of peace beyond the black wastes of the gale; again he heard a man's voice – the frail and indomitable sound that can be made to carry an infinity of thought, resolution, and purpose, that shall be pronouncing confident words on the last day when heavens fall, and justice is done – again he heard it, and it was crying to him, as if from very, very far – 'All right'.

From such material Sassall constructed his ideal of responsibility.

During the war Sassall served in the Navy as a surgeon. 'That was the happiest time of my life, doing major surgery in the Dodecanese. I was dealing with very real distress and on the whole making a success of it.' In Rhodes he taught peasants elementary medicine. He saw himself as a life-saver. He had proved his skill to himself and his ability to take decisions. With this proof came the conviction that those who lived simply, those who were dependent upon him, possessed qualities and a secret of living which he lacked. Thus, whilst having authority over them, he could feel he was serving them.

After the war, he married* and chose a remote country practice under the National Health Service, becoming the junior partner of an old doctor who was much liked in the district but who hated the sight of blood and believed that the secret of medicine was faith. This gave the younger man plenty of opportunity to go on working as a life-saver.

He was always overworked and proud of it. Most of the time he was out on calls – often having to make his way over fields, or walk, carrying his black boxes of instruments and drugs, along forest paths. In the winter he had to dig his way through the snow. Along with his instruments he carried a blow-lamp for thawing out pipes.

* I do not attempt in this essay to discuss the role of Sassall's wife or his children. My concern is his professional life.

He was scarcely ever in the surgery. He imagined himself as a sort of mobile one-man hospital. He performed appendix and hernia operations on kitchen tables. He delivered babies in caravans. It would almost be true to say that he sought out accidents.

He had no patience with anything except emergencies or serious illness. When a man continued to complain but had no dangerous symptoms, he reminded himself of the endurance of the Greek peasants and the needs of those in 'very real distress', and so recommended more exercise and, if possible, a cold bath before breakfast. He dealt only with crises in which he was the central character: or, to put it another way, in which the patient was *simplified* by the degree of his physical dependence on the doctor. He was also simplified himself, because the chosen pace of his life made it impossible and unnecessary for him to examine his own motives.

After a few years he began to change. He was in his mid thirties: at that time of life when, instead of being spontaneously oneself as in one's twenties, it is necessary, in order to remain honest, to confront oneself and judge from a second position. Furthermore he saw his patients changing. Emergencies always present themselves as *faits accomplis*. At last, because he was living among the same people all the time, and because he was often called to the same cottage several times for different emergencies, he began to notice how people developed. A girl whom three years before he had treated for measles got married and came to him for her first confinement. A man who had never been ill shot his brains out.

One day he was called to a couple of old-age pensioners. They had lived in the Forest for thirty years. Nobody had anything very special to say about them. They went every year on the Old Folks' Annual Outing. They usually went to the pub at about eight every Saturday evening. A long time before, the wife had worked as a maid in the big house of a near-by village. The husband had worked on the railway. The husband said that his wife 'was bleeding from down below'.

Sassall talked to her a little and then asked her to undress so that he could examine her. He went into the kitchen to wait until she was ready. There the husband looked at him anxiously and took the clock from the mantelpiece to wind it. At this age if the wife has to go into hospital, it can be the beginning of the end for them both.

When he went back into the parlour, the wife was lying on the ottoman. Her stockings were rolled down and her dress up. 'She' was a man. He examined her. The trouble was severe piles. Neither he nor the husband nor she referred to the sexual organs which should not have been there. They were ignored. Or, rather, he was forced to accept them, as they had done according to their own reasoning which he would never know.

He became aware of the possibility of his patients changing. They, as they became more used to him, sometimes made confessions for which there was no medical reference so far as he had learnt. He began to take a different view of the meaning of the term crisis. He began to realize that the way Conrad's Master Mariners came to terms with their imagination – denying it any expression but projecting it all on to the sea which they then faced as though it were simultaneously their personal justification and their personal enemy – was not suitable for a doctor in his position. He had done just that – using illness and medical dangers as they used the sea. He began to realize that he must face his imagination, even explore it. It must no longer lead always to the 'unimaginable', as it had with the Master Mariners contemplating the possible fury of the elements – or, as in his case, to his contemplating only fights within the jaws of death itself. (The clichés are essential to the vision.) He began to realize that imagination had to be lived with on every level: his own imagination first – because otherwise this could distort his observation – and then the imagination of his patients.

The older partner died. Sassall had to spend far more time in the surgery, listening. He also had to find another doctor to share his practice with. He decided to split the practice in two so that the other doctor should work with his own surgery in his own area. Then, still overworked, but with more time for the average patient, he began to observe himself and others.

He began to read – especially Freud. So far as a man can by himself, he analysed many of his own character traits and their roots in the past. It was a painful process – as Freud himself describes when discussing his own self-analysis. For six months or so, as a result of his resurrected memories, Sassall became sexually

impotent. It is impossible to say now whether this period of crisis was induced by his decision to examine within himself the basis of what up to now he had projected outwards as 'the unimaginable', or whether he entered a period of crisis and therefore decided to look more closely at himself. Either way it bears some resemblance to the period of isolation and crisis which precedes in Siberian and African medicine the professional emergence of the *shaman* or the *inyanga*. The Zulus have a name for this process. The *inyanga*, they say, suffers because the spirits will give him no peace and he becomes 'a house of dreams'.

When Sassall emerged, he was still an extremist. He had exchanged an obvious and youthful form of extremism for a more complex and mature one: the life-and-death emergency for the intimation that the patient should be treated as a total personality, that illness is frequently a form of expression rather than a surrender to natural hazards.

This is dangerous ground, for it is easy to get lost among countless intangibles and to forget or neglect all the precise skills and information which have brought medicine to the point where there is the time and opportunity to pursue such intimations. The quack is either a charlatan or he is a healer who refuses to relate his own few insights to the general body of medical knowledge.

Sassall enjoyed this danger. Safe thinking was now like settling down ashore. 'Common-sense has been a dirty word with me for many years now – except perhaps when it is applied to very factual and easily assessed problems. When dealing with human beings it is my biggest enemy – and tempter. It tempts me to accept the obvious, the easiest, the most readily available answer. It has failed me on almost every occasion I have used it – and God knows how often I have fallen and still fall for the trap.'

Every week now he reads in considerable detail the three main medical journals, and from time to time goes on a refresher course at some hospital. He sees to it that he stays well-informed. But his satisfaction comes mostly from those cases where he faces forces which no previous explanation will exactly fit, because they depend upon the history of a patient's particular personality. He tries to keep that personality company in its loneliness.

He is acknowledged as a good doctor. The organization of his practice, the facilities he offers, his diagnostic and clinical skill are probably somewhat under-rated. His patients may not realize how lucky they are. But in a sense this is inevitable. Only the most self-conscious consider it lucky to have their elementary needs met. And it is on a very basic, elementary level that he is judged a good doctor.

They would say that he was straight, not afraid of work, easy to talk to, not stand-offish, kind, understanding, a good listener, always willing to come out when needed, very thorough. They would also say that he was moody, difficult to understand when on one of his theoretical subjects like sex, capable of doing things just to shock, unusual.

How he actually answers their needs as a doctor is far more complicated than any of these epithets imply. To understand this we must first consider the special character and depth of any doctor-patient relationship.

The primitive medicine-man, who was often also priest, sorcerer and judge, was the first specialist to be released from the obligation of procuring food for the tribe. The magnitude of this privilege and of the power which it gave him is a direct reflection of the importance of the needs he served. An awareness of illness is part of the price that man first paid and still pays for his self-consciousness. This awareness increases the pain or disability. But the self-consciousness of which it is the result is a social phenomenon and so with this self-consciousness arises the possibility of treatment, of medicine.*

We cannot imaginatively reconstruct the subjective attitude of a tribesman to his treatment. But within our culture today what is our own attitude? How do we acquire the necessary trust to submit ourselves to the doctor?

We give the doctor access to our bodies. Apart from the doctor, we only grant such access voluntarily to lovers – and many are frightened to do even this. Yet the doctor is a comparative stranger.

* For the philosophical implication of early medicine see first two volumes of Henry Sigerist's *History of Medicine*: vol. I, *Primitive and Archaic Medicine* (New York: O. U. P., 1951); vol. 2, *Early Greek, Hindu, and Persian Medicine* (New York: O. U. P., 1961).

The degree of intimacy implied by the relationship is emphasized by the concern of all medical ethics (not only ours) to make an absolute distinction between the roles of doctor and lover. It is usually assumed that this is because the doctor can see women naked and can touch them where he likes and that this may sorely tempt him to make love to them. It is a crude assumption, lacking imagination. The conditions under which a doctor is likely to examine his patients are always sexually discouraging.

The emphasis in medical ethics on sexual correctness is not so much to restrict the doctor as to offer a promise to the patient: a promise which is far more than a reassurance that he or she will not be taken advantage of. It is a positive promise of physical intimacy without a sexual basis. Yet what can such intimacy mean? Surely it belongs to the experiences of childhood. We submit to the doctor by quoting to ourselves a state of childhood and simultaneously extending our sense of family to include him. We imagine him as an honorary member of the family.

In cases where the patient is fixated on a parent, the doctor may become a substitute for this parent. But in such a relationship the high degree of sexual content creates difficulties. In illness we ideally imagine the doctor as an elder brother or sister.

Something similar happens at death. The doctor is the familiar of death. When we call for a doctor, we are asking him to cure us and to relieve our suffering, but, if he cannot cure us, we are also asking him to witness our dying. The value of the witness is that he has seen so many others die. (This, rather than the prayers and last rites, was also the real value which the priest once had.) He is the living intermediary between us and the multitudinous dead. He belongs to us and he has belonged to them. And the hard but real comfort which they offer through him is still that of fraternity.

It would be a great mistake to 'normalize' what I have just said by concluding that quite naturally the patient wants a *friendly* doctor. His hopes and demands, however contradicted by previous experience, however protected they may be by scepticism, however undeclared even to himself, are much more profound and precise.

In illness many connexions are severed. Illness separates and encourages a distorted, fragmentated form of self-consciousness. The doctor, through his relationship with the invalid and by means of the special intimacy he is allowed, has to compensate for these broken connections and reaffirm the social content of the invalid's aggravated self-consciousness.

When I speak of a fraternal relationship – or rather of the patient's deep, unformulated expectation of fraternity – I do not of course mean that the doctor can or should behave like an actual brother. What is required of him is that he should recognize his patient with the certainty of an ideal brother. The function of fraternity is recognition.

This individual and closely intimate recognition is required on both a physical and psychological level. On the former it constitutes the art of diagnosis. Good general diagnosticians are rare, not because most doctors lack medical knowledge, but because most are incapable of taking in all the possibly relevant facts – emotional, historical, environmental as well as physical. They are searching for specific conditions instead of the truth about a man which may then suggest various conditions. It may be that computers will soon diagnose better than doctors. But the facts fed to the computers will still have to be the result of intimate, individual recognition of the patient.

On the psychological level recognition means support. As soon as we are ill we fear that our illness is unique. We argue with ourselves and rationalize, but a ghost of the fear remains. And it remains for a very good reason. The illness, as an undefined force, is a potential threat to our very being and we are bound to be highly conscious of the uniqueness of that being. The illness, in other words, shares in our own uniqueness. By fearing its threat, we embrace it and make it specially our own. That is why patients are inordinately relieved when doctors give their complaint a name. The name may mean very little to them; they may understand nothing of what it signifies; but because it has a name, it has an independent existence from them. They can now struggle or complain *against* it. To have a complaint recognized, that is to say defined, limited and depersonalized, is to be made stronger.

The whole process, as it includes doctor and patient, is a dialectical one. The doctor in order to recognize the illness fully – I say fully because the recognition must be such as to indicate the specific treatment – must first recognize the patient as a person: but for the patient – provided that he trusts the doctor and that trust finally depends upon the efficacy of his treatment – the doctor's recognition of his illness is a help because it separates and depersonalizes that illness.*

* For a full study of the subject see Michael Balint's brilliant book *The Doctor, His Patient and The Illness* (London: Pitman, 1964).

So far we have discussed the problem at its simplest, assuming that illness is something which befalls the patient. We have ignored the role of unhappiness in illness, the factors of emotional or mental disturbance. Estimates among G.P.s of how many of their cases actually depend on such factors vary from five to thirty per cent: this is perhaps because there is no quick way of distinguishing between cause and effect and because in nearly *all* cases there is emotional stress present of one kind or another which has to be dealt with.

Most unhappiness is like illness in that it too exacerbates a sense of uniqueness. All frustration magnifies its own dissimilarity and so nourishes itself. Objectively speaking this is illogical since in our society frustration is far more usual than satisfaction, unhappiness far more common than contentment. But it is not a question of objective comparision. It is a question of failing to find any confirmation of oneself in the outside world. The lack of confirmation leads to a sense of futility. And this sense of futility is the essence of loneliness: for, despite the horrors of history, the existence of other men always promises the possibility of purpose. Any example offers hope. But the conviction of being unique destroys all examples.

An unhappy patient comes to a doctor to offer him an illness – in the hope that this part of him at least (the illness) may be recognizable. His proper self he believes to be unknowable. In the light of the world he is nobody: by his own lights the world is nothing. Clearly the task of the doctor – unless he merely accepts the illness on its face value and incidentally guarantees for himself a 'difficult' patient – is to recognize the man. If the man can begin to feel recognized – and such recognition may well include aspects of his character which he has not yet recognized himself – the hopeless nature of his unhappiness will have been changed: he may even have the chance of being happy.

I am fully aware that I am here using the word Recognition to cover whole complicated techniques of psychotherapy, but essentially these techniques are precisely means for furthering the process of recognition. How does a doctor begin to make an unhappy man feel recognized?

A straightforward frontal greeting will achieve little. The patient's name has become meaningless: it has become a wall to hide what is happening, uniquely, behind it. Nor can his unhappiness be named – as is the case with an illness. What can the word 'depressed' mean to the depressed? It is no more than the echo of the patient's own voice.

The recognition has to be oblique. The unhappy man expects to be treated as though he were a nonentity with certain symptoms attached. The state of being a nonentity then paradoxically and bitterly confirms his uniqueness. It is necessary to break the circle. This can be achieved by the doctor presenting himself to the patient as a comparable man. It demands from the doctor a true imaginative effort and precise self-knowledge. The patient must be given the chance to recognize, despite his aggravated self-consciousness, aspects of himself in the doctor, but in such a way that the doctor seems to be Everyman. This chance is probably seldom the result of a single exchange, and it may come about more as the result of the general atmosphere than of any special words said. As the confidence of the patient increases, the process of recognition becomes more subtle. At a later stage of treatment, it is the doctor's acceptance of what the patient tells him and the accuracy of his appreciation as he suggests how different parts of his life may fit together, it is this which then persuades the patient that he and the doctor and other men are comparable because whatever he says of himself or his fears or his fantasies seems to be at least as familiar to the doctor as to him. He is no longer an exception. He can be recognized. And this is the prerequisite for cure or adaptation.

We can now return to our original question. How is it that Sassall is acknowledged as a good doctor? By his cures? This would seem to be the answer. But I doubt it. You have to be a startlingly bad doctor and make many mistakes before the results tell against you. In the eyes of the layman the results always tend to favour the doctor. No, he is acknowledged as a good doctor because he meets the deep but unformulated expectation of the sick for a sense of fraternity. He recognizes them. Sometimes he fails – often because he has missed a critical opportunity and the patient's suppressed resentment becomes too hard to break through – but there is about him the constant will of a man trying to recognize.

'The door opens,' he says, 'and sometimes I feel I'm in the valley of death. It's all right when once I'm working. I try to overcome this shyness because for the patient the first contact is extremely important. If he's put off and doesn't feel welcome, it may take a long time to win his confidence back and perhaps never. I try to give him a fully open greeting. All diffidence in my position is a fault. A form of negligence.'

It is as though when he talks or listens to a patient, he is also touching them with his hands so as to be less likely to misunderstand: and it is as though, when he is physically examining a patient, they were also conversing.

Sassall needs to work in this way. He cures others to cure himself. The phrase is usually no more than a cliché: a conclusion. But now in one particular case we can begin to understand the process.

Previously the sense of mastery which Sassall gained was the result of the skill with which he dealt with emergencies. The possible complications would all appear to develop within his own field: they were medical complications. He remained the central character.

Now the patient is the central character. He tries to recognize each patient and, having recognized him, he tries to set an example for him – not a morally improving example, but an example wherein the patient can recognize himself. One could simplify this – for now we are not dealing with the complexities of the average case but with Sassall's motives – by saying that he 'becomes' each patient in order to 'improve' that patient. He 'becomes' the patient by offering him his own example back. He 'improves' him by curing or at least alleviating his suffering. Yet patient succeeds patient whilst he remains the same person, and so the effect is cumulative. His sense of mastery is fed by the ideal of striving towards the *universal.*

The ideal of the universal man has a long history. It was the working ideal of Greek democracy – even though it depended on slavery. It was revived in the Renaissance and became for a number of men a reality. It was one of the principles of the eighteenth-century Enlightenment and after the French Revolution was maintained, at least as a vision, by Goethe, Marx, Hegel. The enemy of the universal man is the division of labour. By the mid nineteenth century the division of labour in capitalist society had not only destroyed the possibility of a man having many roles: it denied him even one role, and condemned him instead to being part of a part of a mechanical process. Little wonder that Conrad believed that 'the true place of God begins at any spot a thousand miles from the nearest land': there, men could fully prove themselves. Yet the ideal of the universal man persists. It could be the promise implicit in automation and its gift of long-term leisure.

Sassall's desire to be universal cannot therefore be dismissed as a purely personal form of megalomania. He has an appetite for experience which keeps pace with his imagination and which has not been suppressed. It is the knowledge of the impossibility of satisfying any such appetite for new experience which kills the imagination of most people over thirty in our society.

Sassall is a fortunate exception and it is this which makes him seem in spirit – though not in appearance – much younger than he is. There are superficial aspects of him which are still like a student. For example, he enjoys dressing up in 'uniforms' for different activities and wearing them with all the casualness of the third-year expert: a sweater and stocking cap for working on the land in winter: a deer-stalker and laced leather leggings for shooting with his dog: an umbrella and homburg for funerals. When he has to read notes at a public meeting he *deliberately* looks over his glasses like a schoolmaster. If you met him outside his area, on neutral ground, and if he didn't begin talking, you might for one moment suppose that he was an actor.

He might have been one. In this way too he would have played many roles. The desire to proliferate the self into many selves may initially grow from a tendency to exhibitionism. But for Sassall as the doctor he is now, the motive is entirely transformed. There can be no audience. It is only he who can judge his own 'exhibition'. The motive now is knowledge: knowledge almost in the Faustian sense.

The passion for knowledge is described by Browning in his poem about Paracelsus – whose life story was one of the tributaries to the later Faust legend.

> *I cannot feed on beauty for the sake*
> *Of beauty only, nor can drink in balm*
> *From lovely objects for their loveliness;*
> *My nature cannot lose her first imprint;*
> *I still must board and heap and class all truths*
> *With one ulterior purpose: I must know!*
> *Would God translate me to his throne, believe*
> *That I should only listen to his word*
> *To further my own aim!*

Sassall, unlike Paracelsus, is neither a theosophist nor a *Magus*; he believes more in the science than in the art of medicine.

'When people talk about doctors being artists, it's nearly always due to the shortcomings of society. In a better society, in a juster one, the doctor would be much more of a pure scientist.'

Or:

'The essential tragedy of the human situation is not knowing. Not knowing what we are or why we are – for *certain*. But this doesn't lead me to religion. Religion doesn't answer it.'

Yet this difference of emphasis is mostly an historical one. At the time of Paracelsus sickness was thought of as the scourge of God: and yet was welcomed as a warning because it was finite whereas hell was eternal. Suffering was the condition of the earthly life: the only true relief was the life to come. There is a striking contrast in medieval art between the way animals and human beings are depicted. The animals are free to be themselves, sometimes horrific, sometimes beautiful. The human beings are restrained and anxious. The animals celebrate the present. The humans are all waiting – waiting for the judgement which will decide the nature of their immortality. At times it seems that some of the artists envied the animals their mortality: with that mortality went a freedom from the closed system which reduced life here and now to a metaphor. Medicine, such as it was, was also metaphorical. When autopsies were performed and actually revealed to the eye the false teachings of Galenic medicine, the evidence was dismissed as accidental or exceptional. Such was the strength of the system's metaphors – and the impossibility, the irrelevance of any medical science. Medicine was a branch of theology. Little wonder that Paracelsus who came from such a system and then challenged it in the name of independent observation resorted sometimes to mumbo-jumbo! Partly to give himself confidence, partly for protection.

I am not, of course, implying that Sassall is an historically comparable figure to Paracelsus. But I suspect that he is in the same vocational tradition. There are doctors who are craftsmen, who are politicians, who are laboratory researchers, who are ministers of mercy, who are businessmen, who are hypnotists, etc. But there are also doctors who – like certain Master Mariners – want to experience all that is possible, who are driven by curiosity. But 'curiosity' is too small a word and 'the spirit of enquiry' is too institutionalized. They are driven by the need to know. The patient is their material. Yet to them, more than to any doctor in any of the other categories, the patient, in his totality, is for that very reason sacred.

When patients are describing their conditions or worries to Sassall, instead of nodding his head or murmuring 'yes', he says again and again 'I know', 'I know'. He says it with genuine sympathy. Yet it is what he says whilst he is waiting to know more. He already knows what it is like to be this patient in a certain condition: but he does not yet know the full explanation of that condition, nor the extent of his own power.

In fact no answer to these open questions will ever satisfy him. Part of him is always waiting to know more – at every surgery, on every visit, every time the telephone rings. Like any Faust without the aid of the devil, he is a man who suffers frequently from a sense of anti-climax.

This is why he exaggerates when he tells stories about himself. In these stories he is nearly always in an absurd position: trying to take a film on deck when the waves break over him; getting lost in a city he doesn't know; letting a pneumatic drill run away with him. He stresses the disenchantment and deliberately makes himself a comic little man. Disguised in this way and forearmed against disappointment, he can then re-approach reality once more with the entirely un-comic purposes of mastering it, of understanding further. You can see this in the difference between his two eyes: his right eye knows what to expect – it can laugh, sympathize, be stern, mock itself, take aim: his left eye scarcely ever ceases considering the distant evidence and searching.

I say scarcely ever, but there is one exception. This is when he is occupied with some relatively minor surgical task. He may be setting a fracture in his surgery, or attending to one of his patients in the local hospital. On these occasions both eyes concentrate on the task in hand and a look of relief comes over his face. As soon as he takes his coat off, rolls up his sleeves, washes his hands, puts on gloves or a mask, this relief is apparent. It is as though his mind is wiped clean (hence the relief) in order to concentrate exclusively on the limited operation in hand. For a moment there is certainty. The job can be done well or badly: the distinction between the two is beyond dispute: and it must be done well.

I saw a similar expression on the face of a farmer who lives only a few miles from Sassall. This farmer is mad about flying and owns a six-cylinder open-cockpit Czech plane. His farm is not a large or particularly prosperous one. Nor is he part of the gentry. He lives by himself and likes speed. He keeps the plane under an oak-tree in one of his fields. When we had driven the sheep to the other end of the field, and I had turned the prop and he and Jean Mohr were settled and the engine was warm, he signalled to me to let go of the tip of the wing – I was holding it for the plane had no brakes – and at that moment, just before they took off, although there was a gusty wind blowing and the field was very rough and the take-off was liable to be quite tricky, I saw exactly the same look of relief pass over the farmer's unshaved, chunky, middle-aged face. The problems now were limited to aerodynamics and the functioning of a small internal-combustion engine: the problem of prices, mortgages, Monday's market, relations, reputation, would all in a moment be beneath them.

The difference between the farmer and Sassall is that the farmer would like to be able to spend all his life blithely flying and gliding – or anyway believes that he would; whereas Sassall needs his unsatisfied quest for certainty and his uneasy sense of unlimited responsibility.

So far I have tried to describe something of Sassall's relationship with his patients. I have tried to show why he is thought of as a good doctor, and how being 'a good doctor' answers some of his own needs. I have suggested something of the mechanism by which he cures others to cure himself. But all this has been on an individual basis. We must now consider his relationship to the local community as a whole. What do his patients expect of him publicly when they are not ill? And how does this relate to their barely formulated expectations of fraternity within the privacy of illness?

Sassall lives in one of the larger houses of the village. He is well dressed. He drives a Land Rover for his practice, and another car for his private use. His children go to the local grammar school. Without any doubt at all the part allotted him is that of *gentleman*.

The area as a whole is economically depressed. There are only a few large farms and no large-scale industries. Fewer than half the men work on the land. Most earn their living in small workshops, quarries, a wood-processing factory, a jam factory, a brickworks. They form neither a proletariat nor a traditional rural community. They belong to the Forest and in the surrounding districts they are invariably known as 'the foresters'. They are suspicious, independent, tough, poorly educated, low church. They have something of the character once associated with wandering traders like tinkers.

Sassall has done his best to modify the part of gentleman allotted him, and has partly succeeded. He leads almost no social life of his own – except in the village with the villagers. It is when he is talking with his few middle-class neighbours that one is most aware of his own class background. This is because they assume in conversation and attitude that he shares their prejudices. With the 'foresters' he seems like a foreigner who has become, by request, the clerk of their own records.

Let me try to explain what I mean by 'the clerk of the foresters' records'.

'Where you're different Doc is I know I can say Fuck You to your face if I want to.' Yet the speaker never has said Fuck You to Sassall.

'You're the laziest bitch I've ever come across,' says Sassall to the middle-aged woman draper whose day is now made. Yet only he can say this to her.

'What have you got on?' he asks about a menu at a factory canteen.

'Do you want to start at the top,' answers the girl at the counter pointing to her breasts, 'or at the bottom?' lifting her skirts up high. Yet she knows she is safe with the doctor.

Sassall has to a large extent liberated himself and the image of himself in the eyes of his patients from the conventions of social etiquette. He has done this by becoming unconventional. Yet the unconventional doctor is a traditional figure. Where Sassall perhaps is different is that traditionally the unconventionality has only allowed the doctor to swear at and shock his patients instead of vice versa. Sassall would like to think that anybody can say anything to him. But insofar as this is true, it confirms rather than denies his position of privilege. To your equals you cannot say anything: you learn very precisely the form and area of their tolerance. The theoretical freedom of address towards Sassall implies his authority, his special 'exemption', precisely because theoretically it is total. In practice anything unconventional which he says or which is said to him in public is a gesture – no more – against the idea that his authority is backed by the authority of society. It is the form of personal recognition he demands of his patients in exchange for the very different recognition he offers them.

In the village there is a medieval castle with a wide, deep moat round it. This moat was used as a kind of unofficial dump. It was overgrown with trees, bushes, weeds, and full of stones, old wood, muck, gravel. Five years ago Sassall had the idea of turning it into a garden for the village. Tens of thousands of man-hours of work would be involved. He formed a 'society' to occupy itself with the task and he was elected chairman. The work was to be done in the summer evenings and at week-ends whenever the men of the village were free. Farmers lent their machinery and tractors; a roadmaker brought his bull-dozer along; somebody borrowed a crane.

Sassall himself worked hard on the project. If he was not in the surgery and not out on a call, he could be found in the moat most summer evenings. Now the moat is a lawned garden with a fountain, roses, shrubs and seats to sit on.

'Nearly all the planning of the work in the moat,' says Sassall, 'was done by Ted, Harry, Stan, John, etc., etc. I don't mean they were better at doing the work, better with their hands – they were that – but they also had better ideas.'

Sassall was constantly involved in technical discussion of these ideas with the men of the village. The conversations over the weeks continued for hours. As a result a social – as distinct from medical – intimacy was established.

This might seem to be the obvious result of just getting on with a job together. But it is not as simple or as superficial as that. The job offers the possibility of talking together, and finally the talk transcends the job.

The inarticulateness of the English is the subject of many jokes and is often explained in terms of puritanism, shyness as a national characteristic, etc. This tends to obscure a more serious development. There are large sections of the English working and middle class who are inarticulate as the result of wholesale cultural deprivation. They are deprived of the means of translating what they know into thoughts which they can think.* They have no

* My novel Corker's Freedom (New York: Vintage International, 1995) attempts to illuminate this situation.

examples to follow in which words clarify experience. Their spoken proverbial traditions have long been destroyed: and, although they are literate in the strictly technical sense, they have not had the opportunity of discovering the existence of a written cultural heritage.

Yet it is more than a question of literature. Any general culture acts as a mirror which enables the individual to recognize himself – or at least to recognize those parts of himself which are socially permissible. The culturally deprived have far fewer ways of recognizing themselves. A great deal of their experience – especially emotional and introspective experience – has to remain *unnamed* for them. Their chief means of self-expression is consequently through action: this is one of the reasons why the English have so many 'do-it-yourself' hobbies. The garden or the work bench becomes the nearest they have to a means of satisfactory introspection.

The easiest – and sometimes the only possible – form of conversation is that which concerns or describes action: that is to say action considered as technique or as procedure. It is then not the experience of the speakers which is discussed but the nature of an entirely exterior mechanism or event – a motor-car engine, a football match, a draining system or the workings of some committee. Such subjects, which preclude anything directly personal, supply the content of most of the conversations being carried on by men over twenty-five at any given moment in England today. (In the case of the young, the force of their own appetites saves them from such depersonalization.)

Yet there is warmth in such conversation and friendships can be made and sustained by it. The very intricacy of the subjects seems to bring the speakers close together. It is as though the speakers bend over the subject to examine it in precise detail, until, bending over it, their heads touch. Their shared expertise becomes a symbol of shared experience. When friends recall another friend who is dead or absent, they recall how he always maintained that a front-wheel drive was safer: and in their memory this now acquires the value of an intimacy.

The area in which Sassall practises is one of extreme cultural deprivation, even by English standards. And it was only by working with many of the men of the village and coming to understand something of their techniques that he could qualify for their conversation. They then came to share a language which was a metaphor for the rest of their common experience.

Sassall would like to believe that the metaphor implies that they talk as equals: the more so because within the range of the language the villagers mostly know far more than he. Yet they do not talk as equals.

Sassall is accepted by the villagers and foresters as a man who, in the full sense of the term, lives with them. Face to face with him, whatever the circumstances, there is no need for shame or complex explanations: he will understand even when their own community as a whole will not or cannot. (Most unmarried girls who become pregnant come to him straightway without any prevarication.) Insofar as he is feared at all, it is by a few older patients in whom a little of the traditional fear of the doctor still persists. (This traditional fear, apart from being a rational fear of the consequences of illness, is also an irrational fear of the consequences of making their secret but outrageous and insistent demand for fraternity to doctors who always behave and are treated as their superiors.)

In general his patients think of Sassall as 'belonging' to their community. He represents no outside interest – in such an area any outside interest suggests exploitation. He is trusted. Yet this is not the same thing as saying that he is thought of or treated as an equal.

It is evident to everybody that he is privileged. This is accepted as a matter of course: nobody resents or questions it. It is part of his being the kind of doctor he is. The privilege does not concern his income, his car or his house: these are merely amenities which make it possible for him to do his job. And if through them he enjoys a little more comfort than the average, it is still not a question of privilege, for certainly he has earned a right to that comfort.

He is privileged because of the way he can think and can talk. If the estimate of his privilege was strictly logical, it would include the fact of his education and his medical training. But that was a long time ago, whereas the evidence of the way he thinks – not purely medically but in general – is there every time he is there. It is why the villagers talk to him, why they tell him the local news, why they listen, why they wonder whether his unusual views are right, why some say 'He's a wonderful doctor but not what you'd expect', and why some middle-class neighbours call him a crack-pot.

The villagers do not consider him privileged because they find his thinking so impressive. It is the style of his thinking which they immediately recognize as different from theirs. They depend upon common-sense and he does not.

It is generally thought that common-sense is practical. It is practical only in a short-term view. Common-sense declares that it is foolish to bite the hand that feeds you. But it is foolish only up to the moment when you realize that you might be fed very much better. In the long-term view common-sense is passive because it is based on the acceptance of an outdated view of the possible. The body of common-sense has to accrue too slowly. All its propositions have to be proved so many times before they can become unquestionable, i.e. traditional. When they become traditional they gain oracular authority. Hence the strong element of *superstition* always evident in 'practical' common-sense.

Common-sense is part of the home-made ideology of those who have been deprived of fundamental learning, of those who have been kept ignorant. This ideology is compounded from different sources: items that have survived from religion, items of empirical knowledge, items of protective scepticism, items culled for comfort from the superficial learning that *is* supplied. But the point is that common-sense can never teach itself, can never advance beyond its own limits, for as soon as the lack of fundamental learning has been made good, all items become questionable and the whole function of common-sense is destroyed. Common-sense can only exist as a category insofar as it can be distinguished from the spirit of enquiry, from philosophy.

Common-sense is essentially *static*. It belongs to the ideology, of those who are socially passive, never understanding what or who has made their situation as it is. But it represents only a part – and often a small part – of their character. These same people say or do many things which are an affront to their own common-sense. And when they justify something by saying 'It's only common-sense', this is frequently an apology for denying or betraying some of their deepest feelings or instincts.

Sassall accepts his innermost feelings and intuitions as clues. His own self is often his most promising starting-point. His aim is to find what may be hidden in others:

'I don't find it hard to express uncensored thoughts or sentiments but when I do, it keeps on occurring to me that this is a form of self-indulgence. That sounds somewhat pompous, but still. At least it makes me realize and understand why patients thank me so profusely for merely listening: they too are apologizing for what they think – wrongly – is their self-indulgence.'

Using his own mortality as another starting-point he needs to find references of hope or possibility in an almost unimaginable future.

'I'm encouraged by the fact that the molecules of this table and glass and plant are rearranged to make you or me, and that the bad things are perhaps badly arranged molecules and therefore capable maybe of reorganization one day.'

Yet however fanciful his speculations, he returns to measure them by the standards of actual knowledge to date. And then from this measurement begins to speculate again.

'You never know *for certain* about anything. This sounds falsely modest and trite, but it's the honest truth. Most of the time you are right and you do *appear* to know, but every now and then the rules seem to get broken and then you realize how lucky you have been on the occasions when *you think you have known* and have been proved correct.'

He never stops speculating, testing, comparing. The more open the question the more it interests him.

Such a way of thinking demands the right to be theoretical and to be concerned with generalizations. Yet theory and generalizations belong by their nature to the cities or the distant capital where the big general decisions are always made. Furthermore, to arrive at general decisions and theories one needs to travel in order to gain experience. Nobody travels from the Forest. So nobody in the Forest has either the power or the means to theorize. They are 'practical' people.

It may seem surprising to place so much emphasis on geographic isolation and distances when England is so small a country. Yet the subjective feeling of remoteness has little to do with mileage. It is a reaction to economic power. Monopoly – with its mounting tendency to centralization – has even turned what were once large, vital towns, like Bolton or Rochdale or Wigan, into remote backwaters. And in a country area, where the average level of political consciousness is very low, all decision-making which is not practical, all theory, seems to most of the local inhabitants to be the privilege and prerogative of distant policy-makers. The intellectual – and this is why they are so suspicious of him – seems to be part of the apparatus of the State which controls them. Sassall is trusted because he lives with them. But his way of thinking could only have been acquired elsewhere. All theory-makers have cast at least one eye on the seat of power. And that is a privilege the foresters have never known.

There is another reason why they sense that Sassall's way of thinking is a privilege, but as a reason it is less rational. Once it might have been considered magical. He confesses to fear without fear. He finds all impulses natural – or understandable. He remembers what it is like to be a child. He has no respect for any title as such. He can enter into other people's dreams or nightmares. He can lose his temper and then talk about the true reasons, as opposed to the excuse, for why he did so. His ability to do such things connects him with aspects of experience which have to be either ignored or denied by common-sense. Thus his 'licence' challenges the prisoner in every one of his listeners.

There is probably only one other man in the area whose mode of thinking is comparable. But this man is a writer and a recluse. Nobody around him is aware of how he thinks. There are clergymen and schoolmasters and engineers, but they all use the syntax of common-sense: it is only their vocabulary which is different because they need to refer to God, O-levels, or stresses in metal. Sassall's privilege seems locally unique.

The attitude of the villagers and foresters to Sassall's privilege is complex. He has got a good brain, they say, why, with a brain like this – and then, remembering that he belongs to them, they realize that his choice of their remote country practice again implies a kind of privilege: the privilege of his indifference to success. But now his privilege becomes to some extent their privilege. They are proud of him and at the same time protective about him: as though his choice suggested that a good brain can also be a kind of weakness. They often look at him quite anxiously. Yet they are not, I think, so proud of him as a doctor – they know he is a good doctor but they do not know how rare or common that is – rather, they are proud of his way of thinking, of his mind, which has mysteriously allowed him to choose to stay with them. Without being directly influenced by it, they make his way of thinking theirs by giving it a local function.

He does more than treat them when they are ill; he is the objective witness of their lives. They seldom refer to him as a witness. They only think of him when some practical circumstance brings them together. He is in no way a final arbiter. That is why I chose the rather humble word *clerk*: the clerk of their records.

He is qualified to be this precisely because of his privilege. If the records are to be as complete as possible – and who does not at times dream of the impossible ideal of being totally recorded? – the records must be related to the world at large, and they must include what is hidden, even what is hidden within the protagonists themselves.

Some may now assume that he has taken over the role of the parish priest or vicar. Yet this is not so. He is not the representative of an all-knowing, all-powerful being. He is their own representative. His records will never be offered to any higher judge. He keeps the records so that, from time to time, they can consult them themselves. The most frequent opening to a conversation with him, if it is not a professional consultation, are the words 'Do you remember when . . .?' He represents them, becomes their objective (as opposed to subjective) memory, because he represents their lost possibility of understanding and relating to the outside world, and because he also represents some of what they know but cannot think.

This is what I meant by his being the requested clerk of their records. It is an honorary position. He is seldom called upon to officiate. But it has its exact if unstated meaning.

I am very well aware that there is a certain clumsiness in my metaphorical devices. And what do they matter? On the one hand a sociological survey of medical country practice might be more useful: and on the other hand various statistical analyses of the degree of satisfaction expressed among patients after different forms of treatment might be more revealing. I do not for one moment deny the usefulness of such exercises – and indeed have drawn upon many of their findings whilst preparing this essay. But what I am trying to define here are relations which cannot yet be reached by a question-and-answer analysis.

What I am saying about Sassall and his patients is subject to the danger which accompanies any imaginative effort. At certain times my own subjectivity may distort. At no time can I prove what I am saying. I can only claim that after years of observation of the subject I believe that what I am saying, despite my clumsiness, reveals a significant part of the social reality of the small area in question, and a large part of the psychological reality of Sassall's life. The greatest stumbling-block to accepting this is the false view that what people cannot express is always simple because they are simple. We like to retain such a view because it confirms our own bogus sense of articulate individuality, and because it saves us from thinking about the extraordinarily complex convergence of philosophical traditions, feelings, half-realized ideas, atavistic instincts, imaginative intimations, which lie behind the simplest hope or disappointment of the simplest person.

To a large extent Sassall has achieved his ideal. As much as a man can on land, dealing with illness and not the sea, and living in the middle of the twentieth century, he has achieved a position which is comparable to that of a master of a schooner.

He has his relative autonomy and his solitary responsibilities. (Unlike most G.P.s, he has access to ninety per cent of his hospitalized patients, because all but complex major surgery cases go to the local town hospital at which he is one of the house doctors.) He deals with all emergencies which arise – from serious accidents in the quarries or at harvesting time in the fields, to the despair of a young woman who wants to kill her illegitimate baby or the slow suffering and eventual collapse of a retired vicar who has lost his faith. He is trusted, almost without question.

It is true that his attitude to the individual patient, far from being based on explicit authority, is based on answering an unmade demand for fraternity, but this fraternity is *not* mutual: it is an imaginative projection on Sassall's part, as true, but also as artificial as a work of art: nobody fraternally recognizes Sassall: and this makes him the commander.

His position as 'clerk of the records' not only means that, more than any other man, he knows the continuing history of the area; it also attributes to him the power to comprehend and realize for the community. To some extent he thinks and speaks what the community feels and incoherently knows. To some extent he is the growing force (albeit very slow) of their self-consciousness.

Lastly, the area, because it is backward and depressed, is subject to the minimum of direct influence from outside. Its condition is entirely dependent upon what happens and what is decided elsewhere. But very few people, very few ideas – except the ready-to-wear ones of the misused mass media – arrive to challenge Sassall's hegemony.

What is the price of Sassall's achievement?

I do not propose to discuss all the daily irritations and inconveniences of a G.P.'s life. This can safely be left to representatives of the doctors themselves. Some of their grievances are real enough. But the general tone of them is the result of fear and resentment at the sensed but not fully understood fact that the nineteenth-century status and categories of the medical profession are becoming obsolete.

Sassall is not really alarmed by this, for he has established his own special position. As a result of this special position, however, he has to face, far more nakedly than many doctors, the suffering of his patients and the frequent inadequacy of his ability to help them.

It is generally assumed that doctors take a professional view of suffering and that the process of professional insulation begins in their second year as medical students when they first start dissecting the human body. This is true. But the question is far deeper than overcoming any physical revulsion at the sight of blood or guts. Later, other factors are an aid to their self-protection. Doctors use a second, technical, entirely unemotional language. Frequently, they need to act quickly and to carry out complicated manual tasks which demand exclusive concentration. Increasing specialization encourages an increasingly scientific view of illness. (In the eighteenth century and earlier the doctor was often thought of as a cynic: a cynic is by definition a man who assumes a scientific 'objectivity' to which he has no claim.) The sheer number of their cases discourages self-identification with any individual patient.

Yet, however true this may be, the suffering which certain doctors witness may be more of a strain than is generally admitted. This is so with Sassall. He is a man of extreme self-control. Nevertheless, when he was unaware of my presence, I saw him weep, walking across a field away from a house where a young patient was dying. Perhaps he was blaming himself for things done or left undone. He would transform his pain into a sense of painful responsibility, for that is his character.

But his sensibility is not just the consequence of his character: it is equally the consequence of his position and the way he practises. He never separates an illness from the total personality of the patient – in this sense, he is the opposite of a specialist. He does not believe in maintaining his imaginative distance: he must come close enough to recognize the patient fully. Although he has about 2,000 patients, he is aware of how they are all interrelated – and not only in the family sense – so that the numbers seldom acquire a statistical objectivity for him. Most important of all, he considers that it is his duty to try to treat at least certain forms of unhappiness. He very seldom sends a patient to mental hospital for he considers it a kind of abandonment.

What is the effect of facing, trying to understand, hoping to overcome the extreme anguish of other persons five or six times a week? I do not speak now of physical anguish, for that can usually be relieved in a matter of minutes. I speak of the anguish of dying, of loss, of fear, of loneliness, of being desperately beside oneself, of the sense of futility.

One aspect of the confrontations seems to me to be important and not much discussed, and so the reader must forgive me if I concentrate on this and ignore others.

Anguish has its own time-scale. What separates the anguished person from the unanguished is a barrier of time: a barrier which intimidates the imagination of the latter.

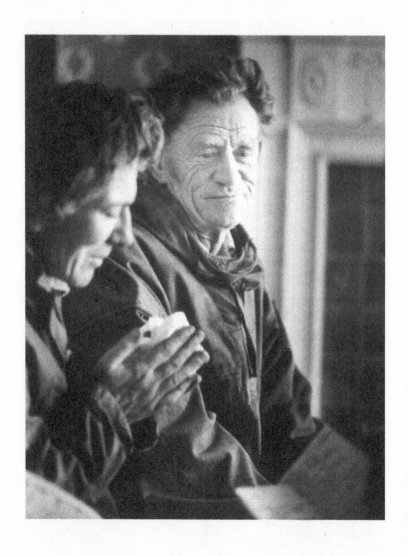

A man or a woman who is sobbing reminds one of a child, but in the most disturbing way. This is partly because of the particular social convention which discourages adults (and particularly men) from breaking into tears but permits children to do so. Yet this is by no means the whole explanation. There is a physical resemblance between a sobbing figure and a child. The 'bearing' of the adult falls away and his movements are limited to certain very primitive ones. The centre of the body once again seems to be the mouth: as though the mouth were simultaneously the place of pain and the only way by which consolation might be taken in. There is a loss of the control of the hands which again can only clench or paw. The whole body tends towards a foetal position. There are good physiological and psychological reasons for all this: but we can observe the similarity without knowing them. And why is the similarity so disturbing? Once more I believe the explanation goes further than our sense of convention or compassion. In some way the similarity, once established, is brutally denied. The sobbing man is not like a child. The child cries to protest. The man cries to himself. It may even be that by crying again like a child he somehow believes that he will regain the ability to recover like a child. Yet that is impossible.

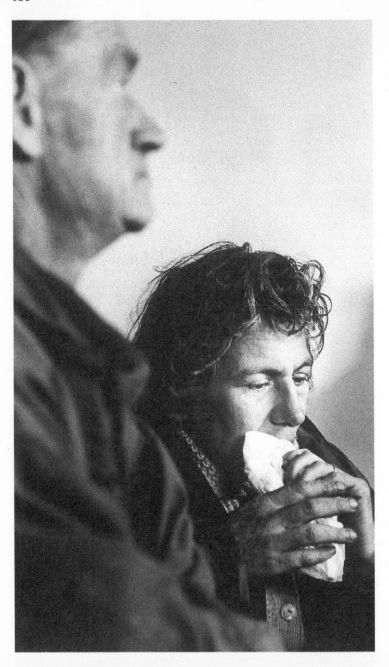

Anguish need not necessarily involve weeping. It may be composed more bitterly in hatred, vengeance or in that half-mocking anticipation of cruelty with which the desperate sometimes await their own destruction. But all anguish, whatever its expression of cause and whether it is rational or neurotic, returns the sufferer to a childhood which increases his despair. Or at least that is what I believe as a result of my own observation and introspection.

It is a platitude that as we grow older time seems to pass more quickly. The remark is usually made nostalgically. But we seldom consider the contrary effect of the same process – the elongation of time as it must affect the young and very young. The young themselves can say little about it, because they only have a standard of judgement when they become aware of time changing its pace and by then it's too late for any direct evidence. If we knew how long a night or a day was to a child, we might understand a great deal more about childhood. Could it not be that the deeply form-ative nature of early childhood experience is due not only to the force of its impact (a force measured by the child's relative weak-ness) but also to the fact that by the child's own reckoning the experiences continue for so long? It may be that, subjectively, a childhood is at least equal in length to the rest of a lifetime. The phenomenon of old people, when their daily practical preoccupa-tions are reduced to a minimum, remembering more and more clearly more and more about their childhood may confirm this; subjectively, their childhood was perhaps most of their life.

Yet why should time seem to change its pace? What is the difference between a child and an adult in this respect? Sartre in his first novel* offers a clue. The book as a whole is partly concerned with a similar and parallel problem: how to achieve a sense of adventure given a full awareness of the nature of time. This is how he describes the habitual life of the adult.

* *Nausea.* Jean-Paul Sartre (translated by Robert Baldick) (London: Penguin, 2000). The novel was first published in France in 1938.

When you are living, nothing happens. The settings change, people come in and go out, that's all. There are never any beginnings. Days are tacked on to days without rhyme or reason, it is an endless, monotonous addition. Now and then you do a partial sum: you say: I've been travelling for three years, I've been at Bouville for three years. There isn't any end either: you never leave a woman, a friend, a town in one go. And then everything is like everything else: Shanghai, Moscow, Algiers, are all the same after a couple of weeks. Occasionally – not very often – you take bearings, you realize that you're living with a woman, mixed up in some dirty business. Just for an instant. After that, the procession starts again, you begin adding up the hours and days once more. Monday, Tuesday, Wednesday. April, May, June. 1924, 1925, 1926.

Sartre contrasts this 'living' with the occasional 'feeling of adventure'. This feeling need have nothing to do with exciting events. It is a form of heightened awareness giving a sensation of order – and therefore of meaning – to the very fact and limitations of existence.

This feeling of adventure definitely doesn't come from events: I have proved that. It's rather the way in which moments are linked together. This, I think, is what happens: all of a sudden you feel that time is passing, that each moment leads to another moment, this one to yet another and so on; that each moment destroys itself and that it's no use trying to hold back, etc., etc., and then you attribute this property to the events which appear to you *in* the moments; you extend to the contents what appertains to the form . . .

If I remember rightly, they call that the irreversibility of time. The feeling of adventure would simply be that of the irreversibility of time. But why don't we always have it?

The irreversibility of time is something that young children are well aware of, although the concept could mean nothing to them. They live with it. There are no inevitable repetitions in childhood. 'Monday, Tuesday, Wednesday. April, May, June. 1924, 1925, 1926' represents the antithesis of their experience. Nothing is bound to repeat itself. Which, incidentally, is one of the reasons why children ask to be reassured that some things will be repeated. 'And tomorrow I will get up and have breakfast?' Gradually after the age of about six, they can answer the question for themselves and they begin to expect and depend upon cycles of events; but even then their unit of measurement is so small – their impatience, if you wish to call it that, is so great – that the foreseen still seems too far off to qualify the present to any important degree: their attention still remains on the present in which things constantly appear for the first time and are constantly being lost for ever.

One of the most widespread adult illusions is the belief in second chances. Children, until they are otherwise persuaded or bribed by adults, know that they do not exist. Their necessary self-abandonment to experience makes it impossible for them to entertain such an idea. The adult belief in them is a double buffer against experience. Not only is everyone given countless second chances, but the uniqueness of every event is blurred over, if not destroyed. And so, as time goes on, or rather fails to go on, we can tentatively propose that the world has become familiar with us, even that the world on the basis of past events is our debtor. Children have no need for such protection.

They have no need for it because their own opportunities seem to stretch further than they can imagine. Their own time is endless. They are constantly experiencing a sense of loss: it is the prerequisite, as Sartre points out, of a sense of adventure. Every parting, however trivial, the end of any game or event, represents a final loss which no repetition will mend. Sometimes they need to protest: then they cry out in the hope that the loss can be postponed, or in true regret for what has gone. I say *true* regret because it is the thing lost which remains the centre of their attention: not, as frequently with adults, their own imagined state of deprivation in the future. Their sense of loss is bounded by the next event or interest. Young children have an almost insatiable appetite for 'the next thing'. The next is needed to take the place of what has irrevocably gone.

There is another reason why young children recover from total loss so quickly. Nothing fortuitous happens in a child's world. There are no accidents. Everything is connected with everything else and everything can be explained by everything else.* (The structure of their world is similar to that of magic.) Thus for a young child a loss is never meaningless, absurd – and, above all, unnecessary. For a young child everything that happens is a necessity.

When we suffer anguish we return to early childhood because that is the period in which we first learnt to suffer the experience of total loss. It was more than that. It was the period in which we suffered more total losses than in all the rest of our life put together. Even supposing that no neurotic pattern still forces us to react as we once reacted on some forgotten but terrible occasion as a child, we are bound to refer ourselves back to that period, for in the intervening years we have only rarely and perhaps never grasped, as we had to grasp continually as children, the iron irreversibility of events.

And yet we are not children even when we suffer again in this way. Above all, we can be aware, as children cannot, of the arbitrariness of our condition. What Sartre calls its gratuitousness.

I mean that, by definition, existence is not necessity. To exist is simply *to be there*; what exists appears, lets itself be *encountered*, but you

* See Jean Piaget, *Language and Thought of the Child*: 3rd edn (London: Routledge & Kegan Paul, 1959).

can never *deduce* it. There are people, I believe, who have understood that. Only they have tried to overcome this contingency by inventing a necessary, casual being. But no necessary being can explain existence: contingency is not an illusion, an appearance which can be dissipated; it is absolute, and consequently perfect gratuitousness. Everything is gratuitous, that park, this town, and myself. When you realize that, it turns your stomach over and everything starts floating about, as it did the other evening at the Rendez-vous Des Cheminots; that is the Nausea. . .

A depressed or bereaved forester obviously does not think like a professional philosopher. But he can see the forest, or the gas-stove in the downstairs room, or the newspapers piled under the dresser in the same light as Sartre describes here. It is almost a question of the light – or rather of how the mind interprets the light. It is a light which objectifies everything and confirms nothing. No child ever sees such a light. It is as different from the light in which a child sees the forest or the kitchen as is darkness.

I wonder whether I begin to make myself clear. Anguish arises from a sense of irreparable loss. (The loss may be real or imaginary.) This loss is added to all the other losses sustained during one's life: these other losses represent the *absence* of what one might otherwise have turned to for consolation on the occasion of this one, the most recent and final of all. Most of these other losses were suffered in childhood – for that is the nature of childhood. Thus the experience of loss tends to return, redeliver one to one's childhood. If the experience is partly or wholly neurotic, the return to childhood is actually part of the experience. If the experience is not neurotic, it is the sense of helplessness which leads one back. This helplessness – equally present in neurotic cases – changes one's sense of time. It is a helplessness in face of the real or imagined irreversibility of what has happened. Such awareness of irreversibility slows down time. Moments can 'seem like years' because, like a child, one feels that everything has changed for ever. The notion of repetition is suddenly removed from the reality of time. In the case of young children this can amount to a form of heightened awareness and is indeed the secret of much of their sense of adventure. But this is because they are able to explain and justify – at least on one level – everything that happens, every loss included. By contrast the anguished adult suffers the conviction that what has happened is absurd; or at the best, is without sufficient meaning. That is to say the meaning which remains cannot possibly balance what has been lost. Consequently the man or woman in anguish is trapped in the time-scale of childhood without a child's protection, suffering a uniquely adult agony.

Sassall meets anguished patients on his rounds – the close relatives of the dying, those who are ill and want to die, the immobilized who are made desperate by a kind of claustrophobic fear of their own bodies, the insanely jealous, the lonely who try to kill themselves, the hysterics; sometimes he is able to reach them: sometimes it is obvious that he never will. In the evenings after supper he has long appointments lasting an hour with patients whom he believes he can help through psychotherapy. They suffer their crises with him and these crises too can mount to the pitch of anguish.

The psychologist G. M. Carstairs, writing from the comparatively detached point of view of a teaching professor, in no way underestimates the stress of such encounters.

To encounter a fellow human being in a state of despair compels one to share, at least in imagination, his elemental problems: Is there any meaning in life? Is there any point in his staying alive?

I believe, however, that the questions tend to present themselves to Sassall in terms of the experience of time. The elemental problem becomes: What is the value of the moment?

It is as though time became the equivalent of Conrad's sea: the sickness the equivalent of the weather. It is time which can promise 'the peace of God' and which can lash and destroy with 'unimaginable' fury. Again I am forced to use what may be a clumsy metaphor in the attempt to define a hidden, subjective experience – the generalized impact on a doctor's imagination of the suffering which he meets almost daily and which cannot be settled by writing prescriptions.

Sassall attends all the midwifery cases in his practice – is present at almost every birth. He is also present at most deaths. He is continually being reminded of how much difference a moment can make and of how irreversible, how carefully prepared the

process which leads up to that moment is. To some degree he can
interfere with the process. He can speed it up, he can slow it down,
he can 'play for time'. But he cannot turn the sea into dry land.

Patients, when their illness has been given a name, usually ask
next: And how long will it take? How long will it be before . . .?
How long? How long? And the doctor replies that he cannot promise
but . . . He can appear to be the controller of time, as, on occasions, the mariner appears to rule the sea. But both doctor and
mariner know this to be an illusion.

All doctors are more than usually aware of death – though some
do their best to hide the metaphysical fact by thinking only in terms
of the physiological stages of dying. In the human imagination death
and the passing of time are indissolubly linked: each moment that
passes brings us nearer to our death: and our death, if it can be
measured at all, is measured by that apparent eternity of existence
which must continue after and without us.

This may help to explain Sassall's preoccupation with time.
What is the value of the moment *sub specie aeternitatis*? But the
confrontation with anguish is even more important. The
anguished are trapped in a moment which is born of all that has
happened to them. Faced with the rigid irreversibility of events
– so terrible for all who are unprepared, and none can be fully
prepared – it is their experience which bends in a circle: unable
to catch time by the tail, they chase their own, revolving in one
moment blindly through all their life. How much then can a
moment contain?

And how can one moment be compared to another person's experience of the same moment? Often it seems almost incredible that Sassall putting out a hand to touch a patient finds the patient there, coexisting.

The objective co-ordinates of time and space, which are necessary to fix a presence, are relatively stable. But the subjective experience of time is liable to be so grossly distorted – above all by suffering – that it becomes, both to the sufferer and to any person partially identifying himself with the sufferer, extremely difficult to correlate with time proper.

Sassall not only has to make this correlation, he also has to correlate the patient's subjective experience of time with his own subjective experience. When he has left the patient and is turning the Land Rover round, preparing to drive off, he may suddenly glimpse out of the corner of his mind's eye the comparative emptiness of that present moment for him, and this emptiness can terrify.

Sassall, except when involved in the actual treatment of patients, is the most impatient man I know. He is incapable of waiting and doing nothing. He is incapable of resting. He sleeps easily but, at heart, he welcomes being called out at night. He finds it extremely hard to accept as normal the normal content of a day, an hour, a minute. His passion for knowledge is a passion for constructive experience with which to so fill his time that subjectively it becomes comparable with the 'time' of those in anguish. It is of course an impossible aim: to construct, to relieve, to cure, to understand, to discover with the same intensity per minute as those in anguish are suffering. Sometimes the aim, as it were, releases Sassall; but mostly he is its slave.

Unrealizable aims possess many men – all artists, for example. The special stress under which Sassall lives is the result of his isolation and his responsibility. He cannot, like artists, give himself up to his visions. He must remain observant, precise, patient, attentive. And, at the same time, he must face alone all the shocks and confusion which have led to the aim. If he were working with colleagues he would never ask them: What is the value of a moment? Nor could any of them reply, if he did. But the question would present itself far less persistently. Their presence would automatically supply the professional context in which the implications of medical cases are strictly limited. As it is, the implications for Sassall can be almost limitless. What is the value of a moment?

I said that the price which Sassall pays for the achievement of his somewhat special position is that he has to face more nakedly than many other doctors the suffering of his patients and the sense of his own inadequacy. I want now to examine his sense of inadequacy.

There are occasions when any doctor may feel helpless: faced with a tragic incurable disease; faced with obstinacy and prejudice maintaining the very situation which has created the illness or unhappiness; faced with certain housing conditions; faced with poverty.

On most such occasions Sassall is better placed than the average. He cannot cure the incurable. But because of his comparative intimacy with patients, and because the relations of a patient are also likely to be his patients, he is well placed to challenge family obstinacy and prejudice. Likewise, because of the hegemony he enjoys within his district, his views tend to carry weight with housing committees, national assistance officers, etc. He can intercede for his patients on both a personal and a bureaucratic level.

He is probably more aware of making mistakes in diagnosis and treatment than most doctors. This is not because he makes more mistakes, but because he counts as *mistakes* what many doctors would – perhaps justifiably – call *unfortunate complications*. However, to balance such self-criticism he has the satisfaction of his reputation which brings him 'difficult' cases from far outside his own area. He suffers the doubts and enjoys the reputation of a professional idealist.

Yet his sense of inadequacy does not arise from this – although it may sometimes be prompted by an exaggerated sense of failure concerning a particular case. His sense of inadequacy is larger than the professional.

Do his patients deserve the lives they lead, or do they deserve better? Are they what they could be or are they suffering continual diminution? Do they ever have the opportunity to develop the potentialities which he has observed in them at certain moments? Are there not some who secretly wish to live in a sense that is impossible given the conditions of their actual lives? And facing this impossibility do they not then secretly wish to die?

Sassall believes that adversity can temper character. But can their groping and sometimes blind unhappiness be called adversity?

What is the cause of boredom? Is boredom anything less than the sense of one's faculties slowly dying? Why do they have more virtues than talents? Who can deny that a culturally deprived community offers far fewer possibilities through sublimation than a culturally advanced one?

How much right have we to go on being always patient on behalf of others?

It is from questions such as these – and a hundred others that force their way up through the pauses between these questions – that the disquiet, which finally leads to Sassall's sense of inadequacy, first arises.

He argues with himself in an attempt to maintain his peace of mind. The foresters are not subject to the same frantic pressures as millions keeping up appearances in the suburbs. Families are less fragmented: appetites less insatiable: the standard of living of the foresters is lower but they have a greater sense of continuity. They may lack cultural opportunities individually: but collectively they have their Parish Council, their Moat Society, their Dart Teams, etc. These all encourage a sense of community. There is less loneliness in the Forest than in many cities. They are, as they might answer themselves, as happy as can be expected.

He refers the question back to his former self – the surgeon, the doctor of stark emergency, who tried to transform the foresters into Greek peasants. The foresters have no illusions about life, he says, only a small minority complain. Mostly they proceed with the business of living undaunted. They do not allow themselves – they cannot afford it – to be governed by their sensibilities. The notion of endurance is fundamentally far more important than happiness.

Abandoning his former self, Sassall now takes a realistic view of the world we live in and its brute indifference. It is the nature of this world that good wishes and noble protests seldom mitigate between the blow and the pain. For most of those who suffer, there is no appeal. The Vietnamese villages are burned alive though nine-tenths of the world condemns the crime. Those who rot in prison serving inhuman sentences which the jurists of the world declare unjust, rot nevertheless. Most crying wrongs cry until there are no more victims to suffer them. When once the blow is aimed at a man, little can come between it and the pain. There is a strict frontier between moral examples and the use of force. Once pushed over that frontier, survival depends upon chance. All those who have never been pushed that far are, by definition, fortunate and will question the truth of the world's brute indifference. All who have been forced across the frontier – even if they survive and return – recognize different functions, different substances in the most basic materials – in metal, wood, earth, stone, as also in the human mind and body. Do not become too subtle. The privilege of being subtle is the distinction between the fortunate and the unfortunate.

Yet however he argues, the disquieting questions return. And the harder he works, the more insistently they are posed. Whenever he makes an effort to recognize a patient, he is forced to recognize his or her undeveloped potentiality. Indeed in the case of the young or early-middle-aged it is often this which prompts the appeal for help – like the cry of a passenger who suddenly realizes that the vehicle in which he is travelling is not even going near the destination he believed he was making for. If as a doctor he is concerned with the total personality of his patients and if he realizes, as he must, that a personality is never an entirely fixed entity, then he is bound to take note of what inhibits, deprives or diminishes it. It is the inwritten consequence of his approach.

He can argue that the foresters are in some respects fortunate compared to the majority of people in the world. But what is far more relevant to his own preoccupations is that he knows that the foresters are in almost all respects unfortunate compared to what they could be – given better education, better social services, better employment, better cultural opportunities, etc.

Talk of the 'bad old days' before the war can encourage a certain superficial belief in progress. But faced with the young – and the prospects before them – it is hard to maintain any such belief. Sassall is forced to acknowledge that, by his own standards, they are having to settle for a fifth best.

The situation by no means leaves him helpless. He can safe-guard their health. Through the Parish Council he can urge improvements in the village. He can explain children to parents and vice versa. His word about a boy or a girl can carry some weight in the local schools. He can try to extend the meaning of sex for them. But the more he thinks of educating them – according to the demands of their very own minds and bodies before they have become resigned, before they accept life as they find it – the more he has to ask himself: by what right do I do this? It is not certain that it will make them socially happier. It is not what is expected or wanted of me. In the end he compromises – as the limitations of his energy would anyway force him to do; he helps in an individual problem, he suggests an answer here and an answer there, he tries to remove a fear without destroying the whole edifice of the morality of which it is part, he introduces the possibility of a hitherto unseen pleasure or satisfaction without extrapolating to the idea of a fundamentally different way of life.

I do not want to exaggerate Sassall's dilemma. It is one that many doctors and psychotherapists have to face: how far should one help a patient to accept conditions which are at least as unjust and wrong as the patient is sick? What makes it more acute for Sassall is his isolation, his closeness to his patients and a bitter paradox which we have not yet defined.

I believe that Sassall's disquiet is provoked, not by individual issues or cases because then all his attention is absorbed in 'feeling his way' and in reckoning how far he can go, but by the constant contrast between the general expectations of his patients and his own.

The average forester of over twenty-five expects, when healthy, little of life. (His extravagant expectation of fraternal recognition when ill is understandable precisely because the illness returns him to childhood, to a period before he had learned to abandon his hopes, and when these hopes could still be reasonably satisfied within the family.) He expects to maintain what he has – job, family, home. He expects to continue to enjoy his pleasures – a cup of tea in bed, Sunday newspapers, the pub at week-ends, an occasional trip to the nearest city or to London, some form of game, his jokes. His wife has her equivalent pleasures. Both of them have fantasies which are infinitely more resourceful and rich – perhaps particularly the wife, who ages far faster. They also have their opinions and their stories to tell, and these may cover much wider ground. But what they expect in their own situation in any foreseeable future is very little: they may want more, they may believe they have a right to more: but they have learned and they have been brought up to settle for a minimum. Life is like that, they say.

Their foreseen minimum is not purely economic: it is not even principally economic: today the minimum might include a car. It is above all an intellectual, emotional and spiritual minimum. It almost empties of content such concepts (expressed in no matter what words) as Renewal, Sudden Change, Passion, Delight, Tragedy, Understanding. It reduces sex to a passing urge, effort to what is necessary in order to maintain a *status quo*, love to kindness, comfort to familiarity. It dismisses the efficacity of thought, the power of unrecognized needs, the relevance of history. It substitutes the notion of endurance for that of experience, of relief for that of benefit.

This makes them, as Sassall is always observing, tough, uncomplaining, modest, stoical. His respect for them is genuine and deep. But it does not alter the fact that his own expectations of life are diametrically opposed to theirs.

It is necessary to emphasize here that we are talking of generalized expectations rather than specific personal ones. The question is philosophical rather than immediately practical. Life is like that, the foresters say. A man may be lucky and have everything he wants, but the nature of life is such that this is bound to be an exception.

Unlike the foresters, Sassall expects the maximum from life. His aim is the Universal Man. He would subscribe to Goethe's dictum that

Man knows himself only inasmuch as he knows the world. He knows the world only within himself, and he is aware of himself only within the world. Each new object, truly recognized, opens up a new organ within ourselves.

His appetite for knowledge is insatiable. He believes that the limits of knowledge, at any given stage, are temporary. Endurance for him is no more than a form of experience, and experience is, by definition, reflective. It may be that in certain respects he is prepared to settle for comparatively little – for an obscure country practice, for a quiet domestic life, for a game of golf as relaxation. (In fact on occasion he revolts even against this: four years ago he had himself accepted as the doctor and cameraman for an Antarctic expedition.) Within his outwardly circumscribed life, however, he is continually speculating about, extending and amending his aware-ness of what is possible. Partly this is the result of his theoretical reading of medicine, science and history; partly it is the result of his own clinical observations (he was, for example, observant enough to notice that Reserpine, given as a sedative, appeared also to cure chilblains and so might be useful in the treatment of gangrene). But above all it is the result of the cumulative effect of his imaginative 'proliferation' of himself in 'becoming' one patient after another.

We can now define the bitter paradox which provokes the disquiet Sassall feels at the contrast between himself and his patients and which can sometimes transform this disquiet into a sense of his own inadequacy.

He can never forget the contrast. He must ask: do they deserve the lives they lead or do they deserve better? He must answer – disregarding what they themselves might reply – that they deserve better. In individual cases he must do all that he can to help them to live more fully. He must recognize that what he can do, if one considers the community as a whole, is absurdly inadequate. He must admit that what needs to be done is outside his brief as a doctor and beyond his power as an individual. Yet he must then face the fact that he needs this *situation as it is*: that, to some extent, he *chose* it. It is by virtue of the community's backwardness that he is able to practise as he does.

Their backwardness enables him to follow his cases through all their stages, grants him the power of his hegemony, encourages him to become the 'consciousness' of the district, allows him unusually promising conditions for achieving a 'fraternal' relationship with his patients, permits him to establish almost entirely on his own terms the local image of his profession. The position can be described more crudely. Sassall can strive towards the universal because his patients are underprivileged.

From time to time Sassall becomes deeply depressed. The depression may last one, two or three months. He is not sure of the reason for these depressions. They could be organic in origin; conceivably they could be part of a still recurring but mostly hidden neurotic pattern established in childhood.

Yet if their origin is mysterious, their maintenance – if one may use the word – is revealing. By maintenance I mean the conscious material which his depressions requisition in order to justify and perpetuate themselves. With the fatal a-historical basis of our culture, we tend to overlook or ignore the historical content of neuroses or mental illness. Extreme examples in the distant past are sometimes admitted. One grants that there was a connection in the fourteenth century between the outbreaks of St Vitus's

Dance and the suffering caused by the Hundred Years' War and the Plague. But do we appreciate, for example, how much Van Gogh's inner conflicts reflected the moral contradictions of the late nineteenth century? Vulnerability may have its own private causes, but it often reveals concisely what is wounding and damaging on a much larger scale.

Sassall's depressions are maintained by the material of the two problems we have just been examining: the suffering of his patients and his own sense of inadequacy. As reflected in his depression this material is distorted, but much truth remains even in the distortion.

He is working well. In a particularly complicated case he senses the number of disparate factors involved, and begins to trace the logic of their connection. He is planning some general improvement in his practice – the acquisition, say, of a cardiograph. He feels himself master of his own experience to date. The extent of what remains for him to do in the Forest is a confirmation of the rightness of his being there. He is always observant, but in this state of mind he notices far more than he can name or explain. Everything seems significant. And the stimulus of this so speeds up his selection and application of a myriad necessary routine responses and checks that he has time to speculate about what he is doing as he is doing it. He is working creatively.

The disillusion that he is about to suffer is likely to be triggered off by a minor setback with no serious consequences at all. A serious crisis could not have the same effect, for it would engage all his attention. As it is, he becomes slightly more self-conscious than usual about his responsibility. Something has not gone exactly as he would have liked for a patient. Yet the patient is quite unaware of it. He remains grateful or continues to grumble exactly as before. It is impossible for Sassall to tell him what he feels about the setback. Not for reasons of tact or medical etiquette.

But because the patient would not understand and would still remain satisfied. Sassall is more sensitive to his patients' interests than the patient himself. He is more troubled by the setback than the patient will ever be inconvenienced by it. Thus Sassall's heightened awareness, instead of supplying him with new evidence and data – as it does when he is working well – suddenly draws attention to its own distinction. He has momentarily reached the threshold of mild paranoia. In the normal course of events the moment would pass with perhaps an ironic comment made to himself. But if at this moment he is unconsciously seeking a justification for being depressed, he can now begin to crush himself in the contradiction between his developed sensibility and the underprivileged life of his chosen patients. The challenges which have encouraged and confirmed him now seem proof of his presumption.

Guilty, he becomes increasingly susceptible to the suffering of others. This suffering, demanding its question about the value of the moment, reveals the comparative emptiness of his own life. To deny this, he tries, as we have seen, to compete with the intensity of suffering. He will work as hard as they suffer. His attitude to his work becomes obsessional.

Soon he is sufficiently depressed for his reactions to be slowed down and his power of concentration to have diminished. It seems to him that he can no longer meet the elementary demands of his practice. The challenge of what remains to be done – even the fabricated ethical basis of his obsession with work – suddenly seems to belong to another, vanished world. He believes that he cannot perform as a doctor on any level.

In fact he can and is probably still, at such moments, offering treatment which is better than the national G.P. average. But he can only partially overcome his conviction of inadequacy by admitting it. And so, to those of his patients who are in a state to be able to accept his confession, he admits his crisis. He throws himself on the mercy of their tolerance. He depends upon the fact that their demands are minimal. The circle is complete. And, as often, the completed circle is the seal of conscientious suffering.

Sassall is nevertheless a man doing what he wants. Or, to be more accurate, a man pursuing what he wishes to pursue. Sometimes the pursuit involves strain and disappointment, but in itself it is his unique source of satisfaction. Like an artist or like anybody else who believes that his work justifies his life, Sassall – by our society's miserable standards – is a fortunate man.

It is easy to criticize him. One can criticize him for ignoring politics. If he is so concerned with the lives of his patients – in a general as well as a medical sense – why does he not see the necessity for political action to improve or defend their lives?

One can criticize him for practising alone instead of joining a group practice or working in a health centre. Is he not an outdated nineteenth-century romantic with his ideal of single personal responsibility? And in the last analysis is not this ideal a form of paternalism?

He himself is aware of the implications of such criticism. 'I sometimes wonder,' he says, 'how much of me is the last of the old traditional country doctor and how much of me is a doctor of the future. Can you be both?'

I wish I could write a conclusion to this essay, summing up and evaluating what has been noticed. But I cannot. It is beyond me to conclude this essay. I could end with another story about Sassall and perhaps most readers would then not notice the omission. It is to reasoning that the poetic gives most of its famous licence.

However, it is perhaps more to the point to analyse why the essay cannot be concluded – always assuming that the obstacles are not purely within myself.

Nothing has in fact been concluded. Sassall, with the cunning intuition that any fortunate man requires today in order to go on working at what he believes in, has established the situation he needs. Not without cost, but on the whole satisfactorily. In it he is working. He is working now at this moment as I write. He may be prescribing a routine cure to a routine infection, he may be listening, taking a few drops of blood from a thumb, imagining himself to be the woman or man opposite him, talking to a sales rep from a drug firm, testing some urine, hoping to learn more, learning more.

I have described something of the situation he has established for himself: but finally this can only be judged in relation to the work he does in it. And I cannot evaluate that work as I could easily do if he were a fictional character. In a certain sense, fiction seems strangely simple now. In fiction one has only got to *decide* that a character is, on balance, admirable. Of course there remains the problem of making him so: and the effect you achieve may be the opposite of what you intended. But still – outcomes can be decided. Whereas now I can decide nothing.

I am in the exactly opposite situation to the autobiographer because he is even freer than the novelist. He is his own subject and his own chronicler. Nothing, nobody, not even a created character can reproach him. What he omits, what he distorts, what he invents – everything, at least by the logic of the genre, is legitimate. Perhaps this is the true attraction of autobiography: all the events over which you had no control are at last subject to your decision. Now, by contrast, I am entirely at the mercy of realities I cannot encompass.

It is true that biographies, as distinct from autobiographies, are also sometimes written about living men and that these in their fashion come to a conclusion. But the subjects of such biographies are either famous or infamous. They are our future prime ministers, or the foreign politicians of whom we must take note. Both reader and writer before they begin the book know why the book has been written. It is because X is the famous X. And the story naturally concludes when he has achieved his present power, which is a form of apotheosis.

Sassall is not such a man.

And supposing he were dead? you might ask. But if he were dead I would write a different essay. It sounds absurd to say that a man's life is utterly transformed by his death, but I mean for those who knew him, or even knew of him. The simplest confirmation of this is what happens when an artist dies.

The painting you saw last week when you assume the painter was alive is not the same painting (although it is the same canvas) you see this week when you know that he is dead. From now on everybody will see the painting you see this week. The painting of last week has died with him. This may sound excessively metaphysical. Yet it is not. It is simply the result of our gift – or the necessity for us – of abstract thought. Whilst the artist is alive, we see the painting, although it is clearly finished, as part of a work in progress. We see it as part of an unfinished process. We can apply epithets to it such as: promising, disappointing, unexpected. When the artist is dead, the painting becomes part of a definitive body of work. The artist made it. We are left with it. What we can think or say about it changes. It can no longer be addressed to the artist – not even to the absent artist whom we have no reasonable chance of ever addressing; we can now only think and speak for ourselves. The subject for discussion is no longer his unknown intentions, his possible confusions, his hopes, his ability to be persuaded, his capacity for change: the subject now is what use we have for the work left us. Because he is dead, we become the protagonists.

It is the same in life. A man's death makes everything certain about him. Of course, secrets may die with him. And of course, a hundred years later somebody looking through some papers may discover a fact which throws a totally different light on his life and of which all the people who attended his funeral were ignorant. Death changes the facts qualitatively but not quantitatively. One does not know more facts about a man because he is dead. But what one already knows hardens and becomes definite. We cannot hope for ambiguities to be clarified, we cannot hope for further change, we cannot hope for more. We are now the protagonists and we have to make up our minds.

And so if Sassall were dead, I would have written an essay which risked far less speculation. Partly because I would have wanted to write a more precise memoir of him, to preserve his likeness. But also because when writing about him I would not have been aware – as I am now and have been every moment of writing – of the process of his life continuing – unfixed, mysterious, only half conscious of its own ends. If he were dead, I would conclude this essay as death concluded his life. Without sentimentality and without religious intimations, I would have wanted him to rest, at least on these final pages, in peace.

As it is, Sassall is alive and working, and my speculations have paralleled the process of his continuing life – anxious to see the maximum possible, but inevitably half-blind, like an owl in bright daylight. Too blind to see the conclusion for certain, aware only of the alternatives.

There is another factor which makes it almost impossible to conclude this essay. It is hard to write about it without making sweeping generalizations about our society and then having to justify these generalizations so that finally one is led too far from the subject in hand.

I must try to be simple. There are such things as national or social crises of such an order that they test all those who live through them. They are moments of truth in which, not everything, but a great deal is revealed about individuals, classes, institutions, leaders. The world at large does not usually appreciate or understand these revelations: but for all those who belong to the society or country in question their importance and meaning are quite clear. Even those who as a result of the crisis find themselves in total and lasting opposition to one another will nevertheless agree that what was revealed in the moment of truth was undeniable.

The word moments should not be taken too literally. The crisis may last for days, weeks, occasionally years. It was like this in Dublin in 1916.

> MacDonagh and MacBride
> And Connolly and Pearse
> Now and in time to be,
> Whenever green is worn,
> Are changed, changed utterly:
> A terrible beauty is born.*

It was like this in France in 1940 after the capitulation, in Budapest in 1956, in Algeria during the war of liberation, in Cuba when Castro landed for the second time in 1959.

If one were writing about a man who had lived through such a crisis and been illuminated by it, it would be much easier to see at least part of his life in perspective, to recognize his historic role. If one's readers had lived through the same crisis, it would also be very much easier for them to understand the value ascribed

* W. B. Yeats's poem 'Easter 1916'.

to this role. To say to a Frenchman who lived through the Occupation that X was in the Resistance or was friendly to the Resistance, or that Y was a *collaborateur*, is to say something about the meaning of X's or Y's whole life.

Sassall has lived through no such crisis. He fought in the war. But for Britain the Second World War did not constitute a crisis of this order. In a crisis that reveals and tests in the way I am suggesting, every man has to choose for himself. By choosing for himself he is then unequivocally committed with all the others who have chosen likewise. It is as though at a given moment each individual were waylaid by the historical process of which he is a part and forced to declare himself. In Britain in the Second World War, we only had to endorse a choice which had been officially made, and was daily justified officially, on our behalf.

Since the war, during the last twenty years, we have lived through a period which must be reckoned as an exact and prolonged antithesis to a moment of truth. We have exercised no choice at all. Certain fundamental political decisions have been taken in our name – without ever being presented to us as a matter of choice. We have accepted them as inevitable or with marginal protest. The Opposition in Parliament is only an opposition about details: fundamentally the two effective political parties are agreed. We have been spared the obligation to commit ourselves to a choice concerning any of the issues which occupy three-quarters of the world as matters of life and death: such issues as racial equality, the right to national and economic independence, the ending of class exploitation, the struggle for freedom (and survival) in a police state, the abolition of famine, etc. We have our opinions, but these count for little even as between ourselves.

Unaccustomed to choosing, unaccustomed to witnessing the choices of others, we find ourselves without a scale of standards for judging or assessing one another. The only standard which remains is that of personal liking – or its commercial variant, which is Personality.

Many will say that this is our good fortune. I doubt it. Our exemption from having to make choices has been so far at the price of the constant deferment of problems – basically economic ones – which vitally affect our future. We will probably continue to defer them until it is too late. Then we shall suffer our crisis – perhaps in Sassall's lifetime.

I am aware of most of Sassall's opinions. I think I can imagine how he might choose in any foreseeable situation. But whether I imagine rightly or wrongly, or whether all the possible situations are foreseeable or not, the point is that any standards for assessing the choice I believe he would make – the choice which may confirm the purpose of his life – are bound at this moment to be subjective, formulating themselves as intimations rather than proper measurements. They are bound to be subjective in this way because in the present situation of exemption and deferment it is only by a personal act of faith and imagination that they can be kept alive at all. Some pay lip-service to a set of objective standards by which historic choices can be judged anywhere in the world: but such people, with wild staring eyes at the window, are all sheltering in various academies of unfelt, dogmatic certainty. By contrast, my intimations, which are felt, can as yet convince nobody – and understandably so. We await the conclusion of the long overture.

Readers who have followed me thus far – to the furthest outskirts of the subject – may now argue: *The future has to be problematic: conclude by drawing up the account to date: let it be an admittedly incomplete conclusion.*

But here we come to another difficulty. Sassall has practised medicine for twenty-five years. To date he must have treated well over 100,000 cases. This would seem a 'good' record. Would it be a less 'good' record if he had only treated 10,000? Supposing he is an intelligent but careless doctor – how much must he forfeit from his record for treating one case, ten cases, a hundred cases carelessly? Supposing that he is an intelligent and unusually dedicated doctor, how much must be added to his record? What would his bonus be?

Such accounting seems absurd. Then let us ask: What is the social value of a pain eased? What is the value of a life saved? How does the cure of a serious illness compare in value with one of the better poems of a minor poet? How does making a correct but extremely difficult diagnosis compare with painting a great canvas? Obviously the comparative method is equally absurd.

Should a doctor be judged professionally – by the consistent level of his professional skill? This would seem to make sense in the case of a surgeon, because his tasks, however complex, are limited. They have a beginning and an end and can be checked. A technique, however fine, is always within known bounds. It would be very much more difficult to judge a doctor like Sassall. However, I do not want to complicate the issue. Let us assume that the consistent level of Sassall's performance as a doctor can be measured as a technique. He can then be graded as a technician. Since with his technique he treats illness, and illness requires treatment, his grading as a technician should be able to determine the value of his work.

But could this satisfy us? The value of his capacity rather than the value of what he has really achieved?

Here I imagine readers interrupting: Of course it could not. But the limitation or absurdity of the answers is the result of the way you pose the questions. You cannot expect to evaluate a man's life's work as though it were stock in a warehouse. There is no scale of measurement possible.

It is true that my questions cannot be answered satisfactorily. But I was asking them to try to lead you to the point of realizing that we in our society do not know how to acknowledge, to measure the contribution of an ordinary working doctor. By measure I do not mean *calculate* according to a fixed scale, but, rather, *take the measure of*. It is not a question of comparing the doctor with the artist or with the airline pilot or with the lawyer or with the political stooge and then arranging them in a winning order. It is a question of comparing them so that in the light of the other examples we can better appreciate what the doctor is (or is not) doing.

When we hear of a team of doctors or biochemists discovering a new cure, we can acknowledge their achievement easily. A new cure contributes to 'the advance of medicine'. The acknowledgement is easy because the promise of the discovery remains abstract. It can be subsumed under 'science' or 'progress'.

It is a very different matter when we imaginatively try to take the measure of a man doing no more and no less than easing – and occasionally saving – the lives of a few thousand of our contemporaries. Naturally we count it, in principle, a good thing. But fully to take the measure of it, we have to come to some conclusion about the value of these lives to us now.

The doctor is a popular hero: you have only to consider how frequently and easily he is presented as such on television. If his training were not so long and expensive, every mother would be happy for her son to become a doctor. It is the most idealized of all the professions. Yet it is idealized abstractly. Some of the young who decide to become doctors are at first influenced by this ideal. But I would suggest that one of the fundamental reasons why so many doctors become cynical and disillusioned is precisely because, when the abstract idealism has worn thin, they are uncertain about the value of the actual lives of the patients they are treating. This is not because they are callous or personally inhuman: it is because they live in and accept a society which is incapable of knowing what a human life is worth.

It cannot afford to. If it did, it would either have to dismiss this knowledge and with it dismiss all its pretences to democracy and so become totalitarian: or it would have to take account of this knowledge and revolutionize itself. Either way it would be transformed.

Let me be quite clear. I do not claim to know what a human life is worth. There can be no final or personal answer – unless you are prepared to accept the medieval religious one, surviving from the past. The question is social. An individual cannot answer it *for himself*. The answer resides within the totality of relations which can exist within a certain social structure at a certain time. Finally man's worth to himself is expressed by his treatment of himself.

But since social development is dialectical and there is always a contradiction between the existing social relations and what is becoming possible, one can sometimes perceive that the existing answer is inadequate for questions raised by certain new developments of activity or thought.

I have never forgotten a paragraph in an essay of Gramsci's which I first read years ago. He wrote the essay in prison in about 1930.

Thus the problem of what man is is always posed as the problem of so-called 'human nature', or of 'man in general', the attempt to create a science of man – a philosophy – whose point of departure is primarily based on a 'unitary idea', on an abstraction designed to contain all that is 'human'. But is 'humanity', as a reality and as an idea, a point of departure – or a point of arrival?*

Is humanity as a reality and as an idea a point of departure or a point of arrival?

I do not claim to know what a human life is worth – the question cannot be answered by word but only by action, by the creation of a more human society.

All that I do know is that our present society wastes and, by

* Antonio Gramsci, *The Modern Prince and Other Writings* (New York: International Publishers).

the slow draining process of enforced hypocrisy, empties most of the lives which it does not destroy: and that, within its own terms, a doctor who has surpassed the stage of selling cures, either directly to the patient or through the agency of a state service, is unassessable.

The conclusion is inconclusive and simple. Sassall practises medicine. His practice perhaps corresponds a little to my description of it. Since we have as yet scarcely begun to establish a society which can assess his contribution socially, since we can only judge him, at best, by empirical standards of convenience, I can only end by quoting the logic by which he himself has to work, a logic which for all its stoicism has in it the seed of a great affirmative vision: 'Whenever I am reminded of death – and it happens every day – I think of my own, and this makes me try to work harder.'

Afterword

When I wrote the preceding pages – and I'm thinking particularly of the last ones which speak of the impossibility of summing up Sassall's life and work – I did not know that 15 years later he was going to shoot himself.

Our instant-hedonist culture tends to believe that a deliberate suicide is a negative comment. What went wrong? It naively asks. Yet suicide does not necessarily constitute a criticism of the life being ended; it may belong to that life's destiny. This was the tragic Greek view.

John the man I loved killed himself. And, yes, his death has changed the story of his life. It has made it more mysterious. Not darker. I see as much light there as before. And standing before him, I do not search for what I might have foreseen and didn't – as if the essential was missing from what passed between us; rather I now begin with his violent death, and, from it, look back with increased tenderness on what he set out to do and what he offered to others, for as long as he could endure.

1999